He was red-gold-and-snow of coat.

What Every Child Should Know LIBRARY

FAMOUS DOGS

EVERY CHILD SHOULD KNOW

by
ALBERT PAYSON TERHUNE

Published by THE PARENTS' INSTITUTE, INC.
Publishers of "THE PARENTS' MAGAZINE"
52 Vanderbilt Avenue, New York

CL

COPYRIGHT, 1937, BY ALBERT PAYSON
TERHUNE. ALL RIGHTS RESERVED.

To My Lifelong Chum,
THE DOG
*Who Knows Much More about Me Than I or Any
Other Man May Hope to Know about Him,
This Book of Canine Chronicles
Is Dedicated*

Contents

		PAGE
Foreword—How It All Began		1

CHAPTER

I	Some Dogs of Ancient Days	6
II	Dogs That Traveled Far	22
III	The Dogs of Kings	53
IV	Professional Mourners	78
V	Some Sunnybank Dogs	101
VI	Dogs of Great Authors	137
VII	Ghost Dogs	169
VIII	Dogs Behind the Footlights	199
IX	"Let Slip the Dogs of War!"	224
X	Some Freak Dogs	257
XI	Some Hero Dogs	281

Illustrations

	PAGE
He Was Red-Gold-and-Snow of Coat	Frontispiece
The Neanderthal Man's Dog	3
Olaf and the Shaggy Gray-Coated Vigi Were Pals	19
Paddy Was on Her Way Home	31
Schwartz	44
Edward VII's Terrier, Caesar	54
Lad Had Completed His Task of Defilement	107
Old Shot	121
Boatswain, Lord Byron's Famous Dog	138
Alexander Pope's Bounce	164
The Rock Descended Crashingly on the Dog's Head	205
With a Goggled and Cone-Shaped Head and a Pair of Wings Flopping from His Shoulder Blades	231
Sherlock Holmes, Jr.	268
And in This Fashion Barry Carried Her Safely	285

FOREWORD
How It All Began

MAN AND THE DOG are the only creatures that worship Man.

Nobody knows why the Dog alone, of all animalkind, chooses Man as his god and serves him with eager willingness. When Man conquered the world, he drove into the jungles and waste places such beasts as he could not subdue. The rest of the brute creation he coerced into service for work or for food.

All but the Dog.

Of his own accord, the Dog came into camp. He elected himself not only the servant of Man, but his pal and protector. It was a voluntary adoption, an adoring, eagerly willing servitude which no other beast emulated.

Much has been conjectured—most of it wrongly, no doubt—as to the queer and breakless bond which links Man and Dog. But the mystery never has been solved. Nor will it be.

The lion, the tiger, the bear, the wolf, the leopard, and their like—these were irreconcilables, from the hour of their first clash with the biped conqueror of the globe. So they went into eternal exile.

Gramnivorous beasts were conquered, and either

were put to work or to the feeding or clothing of their new master. They accepted their lot. But only because they had to and because it was their livelihood. Goats, sheep, cattle, swine, will stray at the first opportunity from the human who has made himself their overlord.

And it is the Dog which—often self-taught—rounds them up and brings them home. He is the one animal which of his own accord places Man above his own four-footed comrades, and herds or hunts them for Man's profit and pleasure. Definitely, of his own free will, he has ranged himself on Man's side in the eternal conflict. Why? Again, nobody knows. It is one of the cosmic mysteries.

By the way, there is one furry exception—and only one—to the rule of "Serve or be banished!": The Cat.

When Man divided the brute kingdom into Slave or Enemy, the Cat refused to join either class. It declined to go into jungle exile with the Wild. It declined to toil or to provide food or clothes, along with the Tame. It declared itself in on every benefit lavished upon the Tame, and it refused to do a lick of work in return. Of all created things, the Cat is most sublimely and unconquerably and contemptuously independent of Man. (I wonder if that can account for the world-old cat-and-dog feud. Probably not. But it is an interesting speculation.)

The Man-Dog alliance goes far back of history or even of legend. Digger scientists have found bones of men and of dogs close to each other in prehistoric cave dwellings, proving the chumship was in full force before the tusked Neanderthaler was exercising the tricky art of walking on his hind legs.

Perhaps, in lush seasons, cavemen caught very young puppies and kept them alive until winter should bring famine to the land. Perhaps, during those months of waiting, the biped learned that the pups had an instinct to sound the alarm when an intruder came near

THE NEANDERTHAL MAN'S DOG

the cave and that they would risk life to repel such a foe. Perhaps the biped learned, too, that the pups were of use in stalking and catching game and that they had an odd gift of comradeship for Man.

Perhaps that is why they and their descendants were kept alive instead of eaten during the lean seasons. A dog had better practical value to his master, living, than as part of a menu.

Perhaps that was the start of it all. Or perhaps not. It all is a matter of "Perhaps."

Yet when earliest history dawned, the Man and Dog partnership long had been on a firm basis. Some of the first decipherable stone carvings attest to this. So do the first fragmentary annals of our race. The most ancient literature, from hieroglyphs down through Sanscrit writings and the Bible, is peppered with allusions to it.

The Bible has eighteen references to dogs. I am sorry to say that seventeen of these are anything but laudatory; while the eighteenth—the Apocrypha tale of young Tobias' walk with the Angel—is coldly negative: "The young man's dog was with them."

The Dog, in some phase or other, plays a part in most normal human lives. From the small boy who drags into the house a canine street waif and entreats the Home Government's leave to keep it; to the aging man who dreams of retiring to the country, "where he can have a dog of his own."

If I may judge by the countless myriads of anecdotes and reminiscences I have had to listen to, the Dog is also one of the too-few infallibly strong pillars which prop the tottery temple of conversation.

Long ago the American Kennel Club issued its millionth registration certificate. When you recall that no dog may be registered unless its pedigree be proven flawlessly pure, and that there are hundreds of non-registered and non-registerable dogs to each one that can be registered, the million registrations may give you some faint idea of our canine population's size.

If you will stop to consider that practically every one of these dogs has, or has had, an owner, you will realize what a stupendously strong element in human life the Dog has become.

So much for introduction to this book of mine. I am not going to carry the Dog down through the ages in scholarly fashion; or indeed at all. I am going to tell you true stories about him.

I shall not arrange these tales in chronological order. But I shall try, more or less, to group them as to subject matter. Thus, Dogs of Ancient Days may rub shoulders with sagas of my Sunnybank collies. And the latter may find themselves sandwiched between Dogs of War and Dogs of Kings—far better company than the lovable disreputables merit.

Some of the stories you have read in earlier and more worth-while volumes. Others, I hope, may be new to you. None are original with me. For that matter, Victor Hugo did not invent the Battle of Waterloo. Yet he built a mighty good yarn out of it. Perhaps, in infinitely lesser fashion, I may be able to retell a handful of the world's deathless dog stories well enough to please you.

I can only hope so.

ALBERT PAYSON TERHUNE

"Sunnybank"
Pompton Lakes, New Jersey.

CHAPTER I

Some Dogs of Ancient Days

IN THE MUSEUM of Pompeii there are two distorted figures, side by side, amid the horde of other gruesome plaster casts. One figure is a child's. The other is a dog's. On the dog's twisted throat you may see the outlines of a collar whose Latin inscription runs:

> *Thrice has this dog saved his little master from death: once from fire, once from flood, once from thieves.*

Because the dog could not save the child from death a fourth time and because he chose to die with his worshipped young master rather than seek safety without him, the two bodies lie today close beside each other—more than eighteen hundred years after the disaster that killed them both.

When I say the dog chose to die with his master rather than to escape, it is not a mere guess. Practically no animals, except those stabled or tied, were caught in the avalanche of lava and of fiery ashes which engulfed the city.

Warned by some mystic instinct they fled from the doomed region at the first slight tremor of the ground.

SOME DOGS OF ANCIENT DAYS

Even as many animals at Quetta and elsewhere in modern times have foreseen earthquakes and have refused to go indoors on command and have run as far as possible from any impending cave-in.

Yes, there seems little doubt that the dog of Pompeii could have gone free. But he could not have carried the child with him. So he stayed on guard. And to this day "in death they are not divided."

Alcibiades—dandy, warrior, statesman and blackguard—seems to have been the premier dog fancier of Athens. He scoured the world for the finest specimens of the canine race he could find; and he was willing to pay exorbitant sums for them. Here is the story of his most famous dog:

I don't know the brute's breed, nor his name. But he was hailed by the beauty-loving Athenians as the most magnificent dog ever seen. His long plume of a tail swept the ground. His heavy coat was burnished to copper brightness by incessant baths and brushing.

Better than all this, he loved his blackguard master with a blind adoration. He was Alcibiades' viligant guard by night, his constant companion by day. Together through the admiring market place would stride "the handsomest man and the handsomest dog on earth," and all talk and all business would cease while folk turned to stare openmouthed at the shining pair.

Things had begun to go badly with Alcibiades. Political enemies were stirring the people against him. He was in peril of exile unless he could stem the ever-rising tide of disfavor. Always in his thoughts was the city's privilege of dooming him to banishment by scrawling his name on shells—"ostra"—and casting enough of these shells in the ballot box. (As you know, we get our grisly word "ostracize" from that unpleasant ancient custom.)

Unless the Athenians could be made to think about something else and thus forget their grievances against him, he was in daily greater danger of exile. So Alcibiades decided to shift the current of their talk and of their thoughts. He was a wily politician and he knew human nature. He hit on a plan which, anywhere except in a city which doted on beauty, would have been ridiculous.

On a morning he and his dog strolled as usual through the crowd of the market place. And as always their presence made a sensation. But today the sensation was of a wholly new kind.

Cries and gasps of unbelieving horror went up from everywhere. Alcibiades was as gleamingly foppish as before. But his dog——

The burnished plume of a tail no longer proudly swept the ground. Alcibiades had cut it off at the roots!

Not proudly, now, but slinking close to his master's side in grieved shame, the tailless tyke cringed before the horrified gaze of the crowd. For a high-strung dog is as keenly sensible to ridicule as to praise. And there were men and children in the shocked throng who laughed aloud at the ludicrous sight.

One of Alcibiades' friends ran up to the unconcerned man and demanded:

"Oh, Alcibiades, why have you committed this damnable crime against beauty? Why have you turned your exquisite dog into a scarecrow? Have the gods deprived you of *all* wisdom? Were the people not speaking ill enough of you as it was? Why must you give them this atrocious new grievance against you? You know how they will talk! You know how they will think!"

"Yes," yawned Alcibiades. "I know how they will talk. I know how they will think. That is why I did it. They will talk of my dog's loss of beauty. They will think in sorrow of that loss of beauty. And it will stop them for a time from thinking and talking ill of myself. They can talk and think of only one thing at a time, these Athenians of ours."

Curiously enough, his prediction came true; if only for a while. The citizenry were so indignant over the mutilation of a handsome dog that they forgot their disapproval of Alcibiades' politics. The project to banish him was dropped for the moment. They could not legally ostracize a man for the sin of cutting off his own dog's tail.

But the relief was only long enough to give the harassed politician a breathing space. Soon his enemies were at him again. A series of misfortunes drove him from Athens. With his loyal bobtailed dog as his only comrade, he crossed over to Phrygia.

There one night his house was surrounded by Greek assassins, sent to get rid of him forever. The house was fired. Sword in hand, Alcibiades rushed out to his last fight. But, swift as he was, the big tailless dog was swifter.

The maimed beast flung himself ragingly on the men who were closing in on his master. Snarling, biting, rending, the dog was pierced by spears and arrows. Dying, he fought on, until Alcibiades was stabbed to death. Then, his human god lost to him, the hero dog at last found time to die. First, he dragged himself in agony to the side of the dead blackguard, and tried feebly to draw out one of the arrows that had stuck in Alcibiades' body.

A grand dog! I wish he had been mine.

Pyrrhus, "King of Epirus, son of Aeacides, descendant of Achilles" (and source of our phrase, "a Pyrrhic victory," because of one of his battles against Rome), was riding back to his palace from an inspection of two of his armies when at the roadside he saw a giant dog crouched whimpering above the body of a slain man.

The dog had no blood on its jaws. Thus it could not have caused the man's death. By its heartbroken attitude it very evidently was mourning its master. Pyrrhus was touched by the creature's grief. He bade his attendants make inquiries. They reported to him that the murdered man had been lying there for three days and that the dog's savagery had driven away all who had come near the body. For the rest nobody seemed to know who the victim might be.

Pyrrhus sent skilled animal trainers to lasso the dog and bring it to him, while other servants should give decent burial to the dead man. The dog, writhing and snapping in its bonds, was hauled to the king. All its four legs were braced, in vain: to check the forced progress and to go back to the master it had been guarding so vainly.

But the king was an expert dogman. He spoke

gently to the poor creature and calmed its struggling. Presently, of its own accord, the dog leaped into the royal chariot and cuddled down in weary trustfulness at the feet of Pyrrhus. Thus the two new friends drove to the palace.

That night the dog slept beside the royal couch. Next day, and for many a day thereafter, monarch and canine were inseparable chums. Pyrrhus had taken a fancy to the luckless animal. The dog, on its part, seemed to have transferred allegiance from the murdered stranger to the king.

Sometime later Pyrrhus went forth to the camp again to review the troops he was mustering for his planned conflict with Rome. As always, the dog rode in the chariot beside him, and then crouched at his side when he sat on the dais whence the review was to be held.

Rank after rank, the soldiers tramped past the dais. Suddenly the dog gave a yell of fury. He sprang to the earth and hurled himself at two men who were marching by.

Confusion broke up the orderly formation of that part of the parade. Soldiers wheeled about to stab the brute which so roughly had interfered with the perfect alignment of the marchers.

But Pyrrhus gave two sharp commands. His personal attendants swarmed forward. One detachment shoved back the troops who were trying to kill the dog. They led the furious creature to the dais.

A second detachment seized the two men the dog had attacked, and lugged them to Pyrrhus. The pair of soldiers were badly shaken up by their encounter with the maddened beast. The accusing glare of their sovereign completed the wrecking of their nerves.

Under a volley of searching questions the last vestiges of their self-control went to pieces. Blubbering, they confessed to the killing of the man whose corpse the dog had been guarding at the roadside. They told of stunning the dog when it had leaped to its master's defense.

Thenceforth, Pyrrhus had an almost superstitious veneration for the big mongrel's powers of intuition. It accompanied him on all his campaigns, until old age barred it from further travel.

And yet there was nothing miraculous in the dog's behavior. All it did was to remember the sight and the scent of its master's killers; and, at the first opportunity, to try to avenge that killing. Hundreds of dogs, since then, have done as much. As you shall see, in part, before the ending of this book of yours and mine.

The King of Albania—or, according to some historians, Porus, King of India—sent to Alexander the Great an unimpressive and lazy-looking dog, Perites by name. With the gift came a letter saying Perites was the last of his illustrious race and begging Alexander to give him a fair tryout as a slayer of big game.

The young Macedonian conqueror was interested in the letter. He sent Perites into the arena. There, in quick succession, he ordered a fierce stag and a wolf and a bear turned into the enclosure, for the dog to try his prowess on.

As each of these antagonists appeared, Perites

SOME DOGS OF ANCIENT DAYS 13

glanced drowsily at it. Then he settled his head between his paws and went comfortably to sleep.

Alexander was disgusted. The show was a failure. The dog provided no entertainment at all. He was for killing Perites, and for disciplining the foreign potentate who had dared to play such a practical joke on his all-puissant self.

Then he reread the letter which had accompanied the arrival of the dog. And he resolved to give Perites one more chance to prove whether he was a killer or a loafer.

In the royal zoo was a murderous Numidian lion, the most formidable and ferocious beast ever captured. He had killed all opponents brought into the arena with him. He had ripped to pieces several trainers; for good measure. Possibly he could rouse Perites to battle. If not, at least the lion was welcome to kill the lazy dog.

The king ordained that this unconquerable black-maned lion should be turned loose against the half-asleep Perites. And the door of the lion's cage was opened.

Out into the arena charged the African monster with an earth-shaking roar. He caught sight of the dog. Instantly he rushed upon Perites. The dog met him more than halfway. At last Perites had found a foeman worthy of his powers.

In the center of the enclosure the two clashed.

Less than a minute later the lion lay dead, his throat torn out. Perites towered sleepily above his prey. The dog had had no trouble at all in disposing of his leonine adversary.

Alexander was thrilled at the easy victory. Never before had he seen or imagined such a dog. From that moment, until Perites' death from old age, dog and king were inseparable comrades.

Long afterward, during a military campaign in which he accompanied his royal master, Perites died.

Alexander wept in uncontrollable grief at the loss of his four-legged companion. He halted in his whirlwind advance against the enemy; long enough to found a new city, to be named "Perites" and to be adorned by a glittering temple erected in his loved dog's memory.

The temple was endowed; and was supplied with priests and with votive sacrifices from the royal treasury. Truly, a sumptuous tribute to a dumb brute which, living, would much have preferred a two-pound T-bone steak as a reward for his services!

Lysimachus, Alexander's chief general in the campaign, was one of the few spectators of the foregoing ceremonies who did not have to force back a grin at sight of such honors paid to a dog. This because Lysimachus had a dog of his own which he valued just as highly.

Soon afterward, in the battle of Korus, Lysimachus was killed. According to custom, his body was laid atop a pyre of scented wood. The wood was soaked in oil and then was set afire, while choristers chanted the warlike virtues of the dead soldier.

Through the throng of loudly lamenting professional mourners bounded a hairy shape—the canine chum of the slain warrior. The dog sprang gaily to the summit of the blazing pyre. There, along with Lysimachus, he was grilled to a cinder.

Pliny has given us the human side of much which otherwise would have been deadly dull ancient history. Moreover, Pliny was a dogman, and he knew the value of human-interest dog stories in lightening and making real the dead bones of historical narrative. Here is a tale from his many true canine yarns:

Flavius Sabinus, a Roman general, was put to death in 79 B.C. His dog had stayed close to him all through his imprisonment and trial. After the execution, the body was laid on the bank of the river Tiber before being flung into its waters.

The dog burst through the groups of onlookers and stood astride its master's huddled body. Thence it snarled at everyone who ventured near; varying this by lifting its muzzle to the skies and giving forth the awful death-yell.

(I have heard this eerie canine death-howl but three times in my own long life. It is like no other sound. May God keep me from hearing it again!)

Says Pliny:

"When someone in that great assemblage flung a morsel of bread to the creature, it caught the food deftly in its mouth and ran and placed it against the mouth of its dead master.

"Then the corpse of Flavius Sabinus was flung into the Tiber. The dog sprang into the water after it, and strove with all its puny strength to tow the body ashore. Failing, it suffered itself to be sucked under by the current, along with the master who had been its god."

Near Eleusis, in Greece, for many centuries stood a tomb in the form of a tall urn. I wish I knew the story of that urn and of the dog whose bones it marked.

For not all the latter-day dog cemeteries, with their extravagant praise of dead beasts, come within a thousand miles of the pathos of that ancient Grecian tomb in its appreciation of a lost comrade.

Many years before the Christian era this dog lived and died. All that remains of him is the time-blurred epitaph which reads:

> *You who pass by! Do not make mock that this urn should have been erected above the body of a mere dog. Such as I am, human tears were shed for me.*

Now let me end this chapter with the tale of Vigi. To me, Vigi is as real as is one of my own Sunnybank collies; albeit he lived and died nearly a thousand years ago. I have followed his gorgeous adventures and life story in the *Heimskringla* and elsewhere, as closely as though he were alive today. Try to like him, won't you, as much as I do? He is worth your friendship.

Olaf the First, King of Norway, harried the coasts of Ireland late in the tenth century with his horde of long-haired ruffian Vikings. Later, he was to be converted to Christianity of a bloody sort and was to sail the seas "preaching the Gospel with his sword" and shouting to his cowed enemies:

"Be baptized or thou shalt die."

But at this time he was only a seagoing freebooter, a sublimated pirate, an apostle of the doctrine that "Might makes Right." It was because of him and his like that the olden English church litany contained the prayer: "From the fury of the Northmen, good Lord deliver us!"

On this raid of Ireland, Olaf and his men captured hundreds of shaggy cattle. As they were driving them toward their ships, a Gaelic kern shouldered his way through the Viking ranks and touched his forelock to the Norwegian raider.

Humbly he explained that he was a poor man, that his sole wealth consisted of twenty cows which Olaf's men had rounded up with the rest of the grazing herds, and that he must starve without his cattle.

He besought the Norse king to give back his twenty cows. So few, he said, could make no difference to the Vikings, but to himself they meant all the difference between livelihood and starvation.

In merry vein Olaf replied, as he watched the milling and bellowing herds:

"Very good, my man. Pick your own twenty out of that mass—pick them correctly—and you shall have them."

For answer the kern blew loud and long on a horn whistle he carried at his belt. Out of nowhere in particular bounded a shaggy giant of a hound, iron gray and powerful. The kern mumbled a word or so to him in Gaelic.

Instantly the hound, Vigi, dashed among the jostling mass of cattle. In a handful of seconds he had rounded up and driven into a compact group twenty cows. No more, no less; cows which bore their owner's private ear nick.

Olaf was a true sportsman—according to his lights—and he was enthusiastic over the hound's performance. From his own arm he pulled a heavy gold bracelet. This and the twenty stolen cows he gave to the kern as the price of the shaggy hound.

Then he took Vigi back to Norway with him on his forty-oared dragonship, the Long Serpent.

From that hour he and the shaggy gray-coated hound were pals. They ate together, they lived together, they fought together. More than once Vigi's watchfulness saved the king from death.

During his sanguinary campaign to Christianize Scandinavia, Olaf chased the galley of Thorir Hart toward a desolate Norse island. In terror, the fugitive sprang overboard and waded ashore at top speed.

Blithely, Olaf leaped from his pursuing Long Serpent, with Vigi at his side; and pursued the fugitive uphill toward a sheltering copse of firs. Vigi outstripped his heavily armored master, and sank his teeth into the runner's heel.

Thorir Hart whirled about and drove his spear through the plucky dog's body. Olaf, barely a step behind, struck Thorir Hart dead. Then the king bade his men carry Vigi to the ship on a shield, as wounded heroes were carried.

My loved friend, Katherine Lee Bates, Dean at

OLAF AND THE SHAGGY GRAY-COATED VIGI
WERE PALS

Wellesley College, described thus the results of the ceremony:

Now proud of heart was Vigi to be borne to ship on shield.
And for many a day thereafter, when the bitter thrust was healed,
Would the dog leap up on the Vikings and coax with his Irish wit
Till 'mid laughter a shield was leveled—and Vigi rode on it!

You see even in those early days, dogs loved a ride, were it only on a shield. Just as the vast majority of them, now, love a motor ride.

When Olaf was drowned in his sea fight against Jarl Eric, the renegade Norseman, and against the allied fleets of Denmark and Sweden, Vigi starved himself to death through grief at the loss of his royal comrade.

As he was dying, Vigi crawled to the summit of a high hill. Thence his blearing eyes swept the country below him.

"He is waiting for his master, and ours, to come home!" muttered the superstitious Norsemen.

Forthwith arose the belief that Olaf one day would arise from his grave in the sea and would come to the rescue of his shattered kingdom. But Vigi died. And Olaf did not return.

CHAPTER II

Dogs That Traveled Far

YEARS AGO I read a four-line item in a newspaper. At first glance its contents seemed to me a right ingenious lie. But for some inexplicable reason I could not forget the item. And I resolved to track it down.

During the next few months I received enough proof of the story's truth to have warranted a Supreme Court decision as to its hundred per cent accuracy. I am going to repeat the yarn here in all its essential details. It is worth your reading.

Bud was a collie. His nominal owner was a man named Coe, who lived in Fort Scott, Kansas. His real mistress was Coe's sister-in-law, Miss Hight, an official in the Fort Scott Gas Company.

(Anyone, with the cash to pay for it, may become the *owner* of a dog. Nobody can become its master or mistress without the dog's own enthusiastic consent. Bear that in mind, please.)

Coe and his wife and their young sons were moving to Albuquerque, New Mexico. They decided to take Bud along, as a companion for the boys in their new home. Miss Hight was not at all happy at the prospect of losing the collie, but she was infinitely less

DOGS THAT TRAVELED FAR 23

miserable than Bud himself would have been if he could have guessed what was coming.

The dog was put into a crate for the long journey, and was lifted into a baggage car. I speak of these details; to show it was impossible for Bud to look out at the territory the train passed through or to get any kind of bearings. He had as little chance to figure out the route or even the general direction of the trip as if he had been shut in a barrel.

From the outset it was plain to anyone that Bud did not like his new surroundings. He moped gloomily around Albuquerque for a few days. Then he disappeared.

The Coes advertised. They made many inquiries. That was all the good it did them. No trace could be found of the missing collie. So Miss Hight received a sad letter from her brother-in-law saying Bud was lost or stolen.

That was in November. One hot afternoon in the next July—a full eight months later—Miss Hight was sitting in her ground-floor office at Fort Scott; when a truly hideous object lurched painfully through the open doorway and crawled to her feet.

Bud had come home.

He was scarred and bone thin. His coat was ragged. It was clotted with burrs. His pads were raw and bleeding. He was a scarecrow. A right pitiful and sick and feeble scarecrow at that. He had used up the last atom of his once-mighty strength in crossing the room to his long-lost mistress.

Miss Hight took him home with her. There she nursed him back to health. It was a long and tedious convalescence. But the wiry collie constitution won the day at last. In a few months Bud was his old self again.

But how had he won his way home? That is an eternal mystery—one of the thousands of canine mysteries which no mere human can hope to clear up.

Get out your maps and study the country between Fort Scott, Kansas, and Albuquerque, New Mexico. The distance is close to eight hundred and sixty miles. To traverse that route Bud must have traveled through endless miles of snake-and-skunk-infested desert where food was scarce and water was still harder to find. He must have swum several rivers, too, and traversed wild terrain of almost every description; before he reached Fort Scott.

How did he do it? He had made the southward trip in a closed crate in a closed car. Every inch of the return hike was over trails totally unknown to him. It was not a question of scent. For home scents cannot guide a dog for the barest fraction of that distance.

No, it was a proven case of the sixth-sense homing instinct which some dogs possess and which most dogs lack. A mysterious brain impulse told him the way to go. And he went. Never had he been a tramp dog nor a runaway. So he had no experience in living off the country or of cadging for meals. Thus he not only had to find his way over those hundreds of miles, but he had to teach himself how to keep alive during the journey's eight months.

Apart from mere food and drink there were mortal foes all along the route: rattlesnakes in the desert, coyotes, wolf packs in the hills; motorcars and dogcatchers and farm dogs in the more civilized sections of the way.

The full account of Bud's pilgrimage, if its details could be learned, would make the most gorgeous dog story in all the annals of scribbling. But we know only that story's first and last chapters. There is but one clue to his adventures:

Miss Hight wrote me that whenever the wolves in the Fort Scott zoo howled at night, during Bud's convalescence, the sick collie would scramble to his feet, snarling furiously, his hackles bristling, his every tired muscle tense and quivering. He never had behaved like that, before his absence; when the zoo wolves had howled. So wolf battles may well have accounted for some of the deep scars which seamed his flesh. But most of his haps or mishaps are not even a matter for guesswork.

Naturally, no healthy and vigorous collie would have needed eight whole months for the traversing of eight hundred and sixty miles. That would have called for an average speed of less than four miles a day. There must have been long pauses in the hike.

Perhaps there were weeks when he was laid up with wounds or sprains or sore pads, in some cave or other hideout. There may have been times when he was captured by some boy or man, and kept on a leash or in a high-fenced yard; until the dog's seeming acceptance of his new quarters may have won for him more freedom and a final chance to get away and to resume his ghastly homeward march.

His homing instinct may have failed him once or twice. He may have traveled far in a wrong direction before he discovered his mistake and reshaped his course. But one may be very certain Bud never consumed eight entire months in steady travel along the right road. All the rest is conjecture.

The rock-solid fact remains that Bud vanished in Albuquerque and reappeared, horribly the worse for wear, nearly nine hundred miles away, in Fort Scott. And that fact by itself constitutes one of the most astounding true dog yarns in my somewhat wide and long experience. More for what it conceals than for what it tells.

By the way, during my task of investigating the yarn about Bud, I received a cheery letter from Coe, in Albuquerque. Coe wrote me he was planning to have the collie shipped back to him in New Mexico, by express, as soon as Bud should recover his strength.

The postal authorities do unkindly severe things to people who send through the mails such words as I would have used in replying to that letter of Coe's. So I left it unanswered. I don't know whether or not he carried out his plan of bringing Bud to Albuquerque. I'm glad I don't know.

Now for a nearer-home tale much less worth-while and much less dramatic:

Here at Sunnybank, nearly a quarter century ago, we had a queer little white dog—half bull terrier, half fox terrier. Someone gave her, as a month-old puppy, to my young daughter. The pup's name was Paddy.

(I don't remember why we saddled a non-Irish female crossbreed with such a name. I suppose there must have been some reason for it. Or must there?)

A few years afterward my daughter lost interest in her. And as all the rest of our Sunnybank dogs were purebred collies of registered stock, we decided to sell Paddy to a family which lived a few miles from here.

The people had taken a strong fancy to the odd little beast. And they had a reputation for kindness to their successive dogs. We were going away that week, to be gone for some months. I heard nothing about Paddy again until we returned to Sunnybank.

Then my superintendent told me the little white crossbreed had come straight home here on the first day her new owners ventured to let her out of her kennel yard for a run. My superintendent had carried her back to them. Three months later—as she seemed well content at last amid her present surroundings and as she had a squirmy litter of newborn puppies— they had let her out of the big kennel yard once more.

And once more she came back to Sunnybank; this time adding to the inquity of her flight the desertion of her small offspring. When it had become a choice between her old home and her new children, she chose home.

Again my superintendent had carried her to her owners, on their pledge not to punish her for her dereliction and to keep her more safely shut into her yard.

He went on to tell me that there no longer was danger of Paddy's finding her way back to us. For her owners had moved to a village eighteen miles from Pompton Lakes. And they had taken her thither in a closed basket.

That was in early April. No further tidings of

Paddy until early December of the following year; nearly twenty months afterward.

Meanwhile, her owners had not let her out of her wired yard except on the leash. On a December morning her kennel was painted. As it had not dried by nightfall, Paddy was chained to a post while sleeping quarters were arranged for her in the cellar.

The evening was bitterly cold. Perhaps the chill reminded Paddy, homesickly, of the big hearth fire with the disreputable fur rug in front of it, at Sunnybank. Paddy had a genius for comfort. That fire-warmed rug had been her delight in earlier days.

Incidentally, it was the first time she had been chained outside her yard during all her period of exile. She explored. The post was rotting. For a time she ripped and gnawed at it with her strong teeth. This, as my own examination showed me, later on. Then, evidently, she jerked away from it with all her might.

The decaying post snapped in two. The upper half of it, some three feet long and weighing seven pounds, held the staple of her chain. Dragging the awkward weight of the broken post behind her, she set off for Sunnybank.

As I told you, the distance was at least eighteen miles and over ground she never had traveled except in a closed basket. But she seems to have had no trouble at all in finding her way to the place she had not visited in nearly two years.

The post, bumping along in her wake, must have been a most annoying handicap. By a minor miracle it did not wedge itself between two trees or in the undergrowth in any of the patches of woodland she toiled through. But its weight alone, on the end of a six-foot chain, was enough to tire a larger dog and over a shorter distance.

In course of time the runaway came to the edge of the lake on whose farther shore stands Sunnybank. Always Paddy had dreaded the lake, and hated to wade more than six inches deep in its waters. I think she never had swum, there or anywhere.

And now there was a skim of ice along the verge. The swimming conditions would have been detestable, even for an unwearied water spaniel with no encumbering post and length of chain to tow behind it.

But Paddy was on her way *Home*. In she plunged.

I was working late that night in my study. Through the December stillnesses came a banging, as of a large billet of wood pounding its way along the veranda. There was a ghostly accompaniment of a clanking chain, and with it the fast scurry of feet. Then something scratched vehemently against a side door. Fifty flying claws seemed to be assaulting the panel. Through the looser noise I could hear a frenzied whimpering.

I opened the door. Paddy flung herself upon me, screaming with happiness at our reunion, and tangling my legs in the loops of her chain as she galloped rapturously around and around me. Never before or since have I seen such paroxysmal joy.

I ought to have sent her back to her owners, the first thing next morning. We didn't need her at Sunnybank. There was no sense in letting her stay here, just because she could not be happy anywhere else.

But I was so mushy-hearted as to mail the owners a

check and an explanatory letter, instead. And nostalgic little Paddy stayed on in smug content at Sunnybank until she died of old age.

Belatedly I apologize for thrusting the yarn of our little crossbreed's homesick questings into a group of much more interesting and noteworthy sagas of more far-traveling dogs. Let's turn to something better worth recording:

Most people who have had the misfortune to reach middle age will remember reading of Owney's exploits. Owney traveled farther and at less physical trouble to himself, I suppose, than any other dog in history.

He was an unsightly little mongrel of unknown antecedents and unrecorded early history. He appeared first on the records as belonging to an Albany, N. Y., postal employee. His master's job was to board New England-bound trains and to sort the mail in the post-office cars. Owney used to make these short trips with him.

That was the start.

The itch for travel began to pringle in the ugly little mongrel's veins. The train rides, the notice paid him by conductors and by brakemen and by passengers, all went to his head. To him it was a far more worth-while life than to stay at home or to follow his owner tamely around Albany. He resolved to be a travel dog. And he kept his resolve.

On his own account he boarded trains bound on long journeys. The crews and the mail-car men had heard of him and they made him welcome. Owney's career had set in. For instance, he would scramble

PADDY WAS ON HER WAY HOME

aboard a train bound for California or for Canada, and trust to luck or to the railroad postal officials to send him homeward again in due time.

Everywhere the newspapers printed stories about the queer little traveler. The Post Office Department at Washington gave him a harness. Also an official pass to travel free on all trains in the United States. Owney was a celebrity. And Owney knew it. He took unpardonable advantage of his official position. His silly head was turned completely by such wholesale adulation.

He traveled everywhere in the states and in Mexico and in Canada.

Then he varied his train rides by sea voyages. He journeyed to Japan—where the Mikado gave him an audience; and to China where the Emperor himself signed his official passport; and across Europe and back to New York; after having circled the globe without escort or under any recognized authority.

In all lands, officials were glad to receive him and to pass him on to his next destination. Everywhere the little crossbreed made himself comfortably at home. In the course of his wanderings he annexed no fewer than two hundred certificates and medals.

His death from old age was heralded as a national loss. His carcass was stuffed by a taxidermist expert and was installed in the Post Office Department's museum at the capital.

I met Owney but once. An unsightly and unfriendly and over-conceited little brute, he seemed to me.

Bobbie was a collie, with a splash of Old English sheepdog. His picture stands on my desk. He belonged to G. Frank Brazier, who ran the Reo Restaurant at Silverton, Ore.

As a pup, Bobbie undertook to herd a straying horse back to his master's stable. As he nipped the horse's hocks, he received a kick on the skull which knocked him senseless twenty feet away and left a scar on his head which afterward was a sure means of identifying him. The pup staggered dizzily to his feet after the kick, but he drove the punitive horse into the stable and into his own stall. That was the kind of dog Bobbie was.

Just as he was getting well from the kick a farm tractor ran over him, injuring one of his hips so badly that there was talk of putting him to death in some merciful fashion. But Bobbie had other ideas. And in a month or so the hurt hip was as good as new.

Brazier had lived on a farm when he bought Bobbie. A little later he sold the farm—and the young dog with it—and moved to Silverton, some miles away. Bobbie followed. Brazier sent him back to the farm. As soon as he could slip away, the collie was at Brazier's restaurant in Silverton, Ore. At last Brazier did as I did with Paddy: he bought Bobbie from the farmer, and let him stay at his self-chosen Silverton home.

Late in the summer of 1923, when the dog was two years old, Brazier and his family toured by motor from Oregon to the Middle West. Bobbie went along. He loved motoring. Most dogs do.

At Wolcott, Ind., the car halted at a garage; for gas and oil. Bobbie jumped to the ground and began an inspection of the neighborhood. During this brief wandering, he enmeshed himself in a very lively combat with another dog.

He won the fight. When his foe turned tail and fled, Bobbie gave chase. And he could not find his way at once back to the garage; he who was destined to find his way several thousand times farther.

The Braziers hunted in vain for him. Then reluctantly they continued the trip without him. They drove to Mexico and thence to the Pacific Coast. There they followed the *Camina Reale* northward to Oregon, and so home to Silverton.

Keenly they mourned the dog they had learned to care for. But there seemed nothing to do about it. So they gave Bobbie up as irretrievably lost. They had left money at Wolcott to pay for widespread advertising. But nobody claimed the goodly reward Brazier offered for the collie's return to his master's home.

Meanwhile, after many delays and false turnings, the dog had come back to the garage; only to find his owners and their car no longer there. There was but one thing left for him to do: somehow he must find his way to Silverton.

Off he started on a roundabout journey which was to cover three thousand miles. He padded across the prairies, getting food and water when and where he could. Through crowded cities and neat little villages he jogged, and sometimes along miles of billowing farmland.

He did not follow a beeline course. South he went for a space, then seemed to realize he was on the wrong track (though perhaps he had followed the tire scent of Brazier's Mexico-bound car), and he struck northwestward again. North of Des Moines he shifted his line of direction and journeyed southwest to Denver. After that he followed a roughly direct course to Oregon.

How does one know the routes he took? Because after he became a national figure through newspaper stories and magazine yarns and books, there were people all along his various roads who remembered him and recognized his photographs. For instance:

When the collie was on exhibition the next year, in Silverton, a man came through the crowd and spoke familiarly to him. Bobbie was overjoyed to see the roughly dressed visitor. Their meeting was in the nature of a glad reunion of old pals. The stranger said that when he and several other laborers were camping in a forest near White River, in September of 1923, Bobbie had come into camp one day and had made himself thoroughly at home there.

The dog had been bone thin and he seemed exhausted and half starved. The campers made him welcome. They fed him and let him sleep by the fire. For some days he stayed on with them. They became genuinely fond of him. Then he had gone away.

Farmers' wives in several parts of the country recalled feeding and sheltering him. Folk told of seeing him plodding wearily through some town. In course of time, his hike's route was solidly established.

He had panted in cruelly hot desert sands. He had waded through swamps and skirted wide lakes and had swum rivers. He had climbed the Rockies, braving blizzards and ice; menaced by wolf and bear and mountain lion.

Whenever his strength gave out he would invite himself to the home of the first kindhearted person he could find. There he would stay (as in the forest camp) until he was rested and strong again and until his sore pads healed. Then he would take up his tedious quest.

He had been lost at Wolcott, Ind., on August 15, 1923. On February 15, 1924, precisely six months later, he staggered into Brazier's house at Silverton, Ore., so exhausted that he could not get to his feet unaided for more than a week thereafter.

It would be monstrous pleasant to end the story of Bobbie by saying he was allowed to spend the rest of his days in tranquil happiness with the master he had risked life to rejoin. But that was not the way it worked out.

For the newspapers, from Maine to Los Angeles, played up the astonishing exploit. And the public came a-running.

Bobbie was exhibited. Thousands of people crowded to gaze on the wonder dog. They patted and mauled him until his tender flesh was so badly pinched and bruised that Brazier rigged up a wire screen between the suffering brute and his milling horde of admirers.

Idiotic gifts were showered upon him from everywhere; gifts ranging from a gold collar and a slew of shiny medals to elaborately engrossed scrolls. And the bemused dog would gleefully have swapped the whole absurd collection of trinkets for one pound of lean raw beef! It was all a damnable ordeal for the high-strung collie.

As his first gush of fame began to die down, it was fanned to momentary life again by another widely published newspaper yarn.

As Bobbie and Brazier were walking through the woods near Silverton, the dog dashed toward a pile of cut underbrush. Around and around it he galloped, barking and whining in stark excitement. Then he rushed at it and tried to pull it to pieces. Men investigated the heap of bushes.

It covered the body of a suicide.

When Washington was encamped at Morristown, N. J., during the Revolutionary War, a valuable pointer dog strayed all the way from New York, swimming the Hudson, and wandered into the Chief's headquarters.

A staff officer reported to Washington in high glee that at last the patriots had a British prisoner whose loss would cause deep grief to the enemy's commander. He said the pointer had been recognized as the priceless and beloved dog of General Howe, in command of the British forces in New York, and that Howe had offered a fabulous reward for the animal's restoration.

There was much merriment at headquarters at thought of Howe's chagrin and at Washington's acquiring such a splendid dog. But Washington cut short the mirth. He sent the pointer back to Howe, under a flag of truce, and with the message that it was a pleasure to reunite so fine a dog and so gallant an officer.

So runs the accepted version of the incident. Indeed, Jerseymen saw a divine omen in the fact that the British general's favorite dog should desert to the American cause and that he should swim a wide river and journey through many miles thereafter and "come into camp" of his own accord.

I have told the tale as it has appeared often in print.

And I don't believe a word of it.

To me it seems a hundredfold more likely that some patriot in New York should have sought to spite and grieve the hated British commander by stealing his treasured dog and smuggling it to Washington's Morristown camp. That version of the story makes sense to me. The accepted version leans too heavily on the long arm of coincidence.

More than once on my crosscountry hikes and roadside walks I have met such a dog of passage. Not the lost dog that roams uncertainly, running up to every stranger in the hope it may be his missing master, or slinking guiltily out of sight, but the dog that trots steadily, swervelessly, intent on his own business and paying no attention to anyone; the dog that has a goal to reach.

A few such dogs in past years have stopped at Sunnybank to eat and to rest. There was nothing of the tramp dog in their demeanor. They had come to a point where they must rest and eat before they could go on. I have fed and sheltered them willingly. And when they were able to travel again they took up their pilgrimage anew.

These dogs of passage seem to me among the most pathetic creatures in all the animal kingdom. The more so because even the best-intentioned human can do nothing to aid them in their quest except to give them food and a momentary resting place.

Just now I spoke of the possibility that Bobbie may have caught the scent of his owner's car tires. To a novice the theory may sound ridiculous. But I could cite fifty authentic instances to prove it is not. It is true, and no theory at all. Not all dogs can follow a car by the scent of its tire tracks. Probably most of them can't. But many can.

Here is an instance of the kind. An instance which ties up with the story of a dog of passage. It appeared in all the newspapers, back in the middle 1920's.

My blue-ribbon collie, Sunnybank Explorer, lacked but three of the fifteen points to make him a Champion of Record—points that he won a year or so after the following adventure of his. I wanted to put him through to his championship that spring—I think it was in 1926. There were one or two promising dog shows to be held in northern New York State. I was hard pressed with work just then. I could not spare the time to make the rounds of these shows.

So, for the first and last time in my life, I put a dog in charge of a professional handler, a handler I knew to be kind and reliable and whom my dogs liked. I motored Explorer to this handler's kennels and left him there, to be carried to the show or shows which should give him his needed three championship points. Then I drove back to Sunnybank.

That night the kennelman went into the shed where the collie was quartered, to carry his dinner to him. Explorer dived out between the man's legs and was swallowed up in the darkness. Early next day I was notified of the mishap. I drove to the kennels at once. It was a long trip. I kept a sharp lookout on every side for sign of my missing collie. I stopped at a dozen places, police stations and the like, to make inquiries. But I drew blank.

When I reached the handler's, I drove up to the side of the porch and stepped directly to the veranda from the car, without my feet touching the ground. When I left, I stepped once more across the narrow space without putting foot to the ground. Then I drove home.

You will see presently why I tell these dull details of my trip to such length.

Now this is what Explorer had been doing after his escape: (As with Bobbie, his progress was seen and noted by several people along the line of travel.)

When he dived to freedom, between the kennelman's legs, he set off in a fairly straight line for home, traveling cross-country part of the way and part of the way by road. It chanced to be a different road from the one I took next morning.

After a long time the collie came to the edge of the Hudson River, near Tarrytown. At that point the river widens into what is known as the Tappan Zee: a stretch of water several miles in extent. And here Explorer paused. He began to cast up and down stream. Then he circled, nose to ground, in widening arcs.

A dog's scent is miraculously keen. His hearing, too, is far more acute than is yours. But his sight is not good. At night he can see much better than can a human. But by daylight he cannot see very far. Sight is the weakest of his senses.

Thus when Explorer came to the brink of the Tappan Zee he could not possibly see across to the other side, whence it was a bare twenty-one miles to Sunnybank. It was as though a man should come to the edge of a boatless ocean in the course of a journey.

So the collie circled, and cast about for some means of skirting this illimitable sea. If his vision could have reached to the far side of the stream he might have swum for the other shore. But he had no way of guessing that the water might not extend for a thousand miles. And Explorer was neither a fool nor a suicide. So he stayed on the eastern bank.

As he was casting around, he caught the track of my tires. And he followed them all the way to the distant kennels whence he had escaped. It is a miracle some motorist on the way did not hit and kill him. He reached the handler's house soon after I had left by another road. The tracks led to the porch. Mounting that, the dog caught the more familiar scent of my footsteps. They led him to the doorway I had entered. As they were not on the ground or anywhere else but in that one straight line, the dog must have assumed I still was in the house at whose threshold the trail scent ended.

Accordingly, he lay down on the door mat to wait patiently until I should come out again. Which, I think, savors strongly of human deductive reasoning. Even if, like so much of human deductive reasoning, it was built on a stratum of fallacies.

Hours afterward the handler found him lying there, on the mat, still waiting for me to come out of the house where my trail stopped short.

Before I received the telephone message telling me of the collie's safety I had sent an advertisement to the New York papers offering a reward of $100 for Explorer's return or for tidings which would lead to my finding him. I added a full description of the dog. I would have offered much more cash—for he was worth several hundred dollars—but I feared the sum might rouse doubt of my good faith.

As it was, I received a sheaf of letters from persons who had seen him somewhere along the way. From these letters, as well as from later news, I reconstructed easily every stage of his frustrated effort to come home. The handler ended the telephone announcement of his recovery by saying:

"He's none the worse for his trip. We'll make a champion of him inside of a fortnight, at most. I'm starting for Buffalo with him tomorrow. Mrs Lunt is judging there. She likes his slashing type of collie. It will be at least a three-point show."

To which I replied somewhat ungraciously:

"You'll do nothing of the kind. I'm driving up to your kennels today to bring him home. Later, I'll take him to the autumn shows, myself, for a championship try. Till then I'd rather have a live chum than a dead champion. Buffalo is nearly five hundred miles from Sunnybank. If he got away from you again, up there, he might have more trouble in finding his way back to me."

One more—and inordinately a more interesting and dramatic tale of a dog of passage—and this chapter will end. I beg you will read this last anecdote. For,

SCHWARTZ

in its way, it is one of the strangest and best true dog stories I know of.

Perhaps you have read the story of Schwartz. More than once it has appeared in print, both in this country and in Europe. Also I have told it over the radio and in a magazine.

Schwartz was a black poodle—member of a breed uncannily clever and too little appreciated in this country. He belonged to a German professor who lectured at Heidelberg. Directly across from the professor's house was a tobacco shop. From puppyhood, Schwartz had been taught to go every day to this shop and to fetch back to his master a packet of the latter's favorite brand of pipe tobacco.

It was a simple trick, this tobacco-fetching; so simple that Schwartz had learned it in a single lesson. But it was amusing in its way, and it saved the professor a great many steps in the course of the years.

Neighbors used to call strangers to watch the black poodle trot across to the shop, there to rest his forepaws on the counter and accept gingerly the packet and carry it home.

The dog was inordinately proud of this accomplishment and he reveled in the praise it used to evoke.

Then the professor moved to a city about one hundred and fifty miles from Heidelberg. A tobacco shop chanced to be directly across the street from the house he rented there. It was a shop precisely like the one opposite his home in Heidelberg.

This coincidence pleased the professor. For now he could get his daily packet of pipe tobacco in the same easy way: by sending Schwartz across for it. Incidentally the black poodle would win fame all over again for his knack at fetching.

A charge account was arranged and the tobacconist was told to be on the lookout for the messenger dog each morning. This on the day the professor moved into his newly rented house.

After early breakfast the following morning, he went to the front door with the poodle, as he had done for years, and said:

"Schwartz! Tobacco!"

Always this had been the signal for the dog to dance in gay excitement and then to dash across to the tobacconist's on his happy errand. There had been snap and verve and gladness in his every motion. But today he stared up at his owner in blinking bewilderment. He seemed not to understand the long-familiar command.

The man repeated it, somewhat impatiently. He had bragged much to the tobacconist of his poodle's cleverness. He knew there would be folk in the shop waiting to see the performance. He could not understand his dog's scared stupidity. A third time, and louder, he said:

"Tobacco! Schwartz! *Tobacco!*"

This time he saw that the poodle understood. There could be no doubt as to that. But in place of his oldtime joy in obeying, Schwartz flattened his black body to the floor of the threshold. He was quivering all over, as if with a congestive chill.

Under his breath he was moaning piteously. His dark eyes were upraised to his master in an anguish of appeal for mercy. For an instant the professor stared at him in amazement. Then came memory of the people waiting in the tobacco shop across the street, and the ridicule which must follow the collapse of all his bragging about Schwartz.

A gust of hot rage swept away his moment of perplexity. Bellowing the command afresh, he landed a breath-expelling kick on the ribs of the groveling and terror-stricken poodle.

It was the first time in his happy life that Schwartz had been punished. It was the first time he had been bellowed at by his loved master.

He did not flinch from kick or from shout.

Instead, he rose slowly to his feet, his eyes still fixed on the man's. He licked his owner's hand timidly. Then he trotted down the steps and into the street.

DOGS THAT TRAVELED FAR 47

The professor, still fuming, slammed shut the front door and stamped back to his study. In another five minutes, at most, he was certain, Schwartz would give his customary glad whine and would scratch at the door for admittance. And he would frisk over to his master and drop the tobacco packet in the latter's outstretched palm.

This he had done every weekday for three years. This assuredly he would do again today.

And this is what Schwartz did *not* do. As the professor might have foreseen, if he had taken half as much trouble to delve into canine nature as into his dusty and fusty classroom research books.

The five minutes crept by. Then an hour crawled past. Fuming once more, the professor made his way to the tobacconist's on the opposite side of the street. Schwartz had not been there. The knot of neighbors who had assembled to watch him do his pretty trick had dispersed amid much derision.

The professor could not understand. It was the first time his poodle had failed him. Then he hit on a possible solution: A thief had stolen the dog on the way across the street. Perhaps Schwartz had had an intuition that some such thing would happen. That might have accounted for his unwillingness to go. The man had read that dogs sometimes have queer hunches like that.

But he valued Schwartz. So he advertised for him in the local papers and he told the police and he made inquiries everywhere and he searched the streets and alleys for miles around.

He drew blank.

Schwartz apparently had melted into more or less thin air. There was no clue. The reward offered was big enough to have tempted the most grasping dog thief. But it evoked not a single nibble. Of course, as ever in such cases, several wholly honest persons who read the advertisements brought to the professor's door batches of stray dogs they had found; and asked if Schwartz was one of the cringing Assembly of the Lost.

He was not.

Now let me spoil the suspense of this anecdote by giving you a glimpse of what had gone on (as later was proven) in Schwartz's brain when his master had said with increasing vehemence and bad temper: *"Schwartz! Tobacco!"*

A dog cannot read. To him one shop's sign is like another's. Schwartz had no means of guessing that the shop across the street was a tobacconist's. More than a thousand times in the past three years the professor had given that command. Always it had meant one thing and one thing alone; the meaning he had taught to Schwartz as a puppy:

It meant the black poodle was to go to the shop on the Heidelberg street opposite his owner's old home. He was to push open the shop's swing door and trot thence to the counter. He was to rear himself on his hind legs and brace his fore paws on the counter. The clerk was to put a packet of pipe tobacco between his invitingly open jaws. This packet Schwartz was to carry home. Then he was to lay it in his master's outthrust palm.

To him, there was but one tobacconist's shop in the

world. That shop was in Heidelberg. And in a far-distant strange city the professor had bidden him go to this shop!

Small wonder he could not credit his own hearing when first the order was given! Still less wonder that he shrank in terror when at last the sense of the words was made plain to him and was enforced by an agonizing kick in the ribs!

Yet when all dumb pleas for mercy had failed it did not occur to the poodle to disobey this murderously cruel command of the man who was his god. So he had gone forth upon his mission.

He had begun a hundred-and-fifty-mile trek, on foot, to Heidelberg and to the tobacco shop there, in quest of the packet his owner had bidden him fetch home.

To those of you who are not dog folk, the foregoing line of canine reasoning may at first sound far-fetched and absurd. Anyone who has studied dogs will understand that its logical sequences are flawlessly normal. In any event, the results proved that this was Schwartz's line of thought. Do you wonder he cringed at the prospect it implied?

Ten days after he disappeared, Schwartz came back to his master's new home.

As the professor sat at breakfast, he heard a feeble whine and a feebler scratching at the door—a ghost of the proud clamor whereby Schwartz hitherto had proclaimed his return from the tobacconist's with his fresh packet of pipe fodder.

The professor flung wide the door. On the top steps lay his black poodle. The dog had collapsed. His scratched announcement of his return had used up all his remaining half-grain of vitality. Yet at sight of the man bending above him, he raised himself weakly and with tremendous effort to a crouching posture.

Into the palm of the professor's caressing hand the dog dropped a wet and shrunken and nearly empty muslin bag—a bag bearing the label of the Heidelberg tobacconist.

Schwartz's mission was accomplished. He had achieved the impossible. He had obeyed the professor's thoughtlessly horrible command. He had run his errand. He had come home with the package he had been sent to get. At long last the dog now had time to do the only thing he yearned to do: To die.

He slumped dead across his master's feet.

Afterward came a series of letters and replies and a traversing of the one-hundred-and-fifty-mile route by the professor and a questioning of people along the line of travel. Here are the net results of the inquiries:

Schwartz had set out for Heidelberg, his deity's command ringing in his ears, his deity's kick throbbing in his ribs. How did he guess the right road to Heidelberg? *I* don't know. How did Bud guess the way from Albuquerque to Fort Scott? How did Paddy guess the way from Whippany, N. J., to Sunnybank? How did any of innumerable dogs find their way to their old homes?

By some means occult to us humans—as simple to some dogs as is the working of a radio machine to you—Schwartz had found his way to Heidelberg. There he had limped at once, hungry and worn out, to the tobacconist from whom he had received his packet of tobacco six times a week for several months above three years—more than one thousand times in all—and he had upreared his bleeding forepaws on the counter.

The tobacconist supposed (as he declared afterward) that the professor had moved back to Heidelberg and had sent his poodle for the daily supply of that special brand of pipe tobacco. He had put a muslin sack of it into Schwartz's mouth.

Wearily the poor dog had started back on his one-hundred-and-fifty-mile return journey. Along the route he had had to drop the sack, more than once, to drink (he does not seem to have eaten) or to fight off village curs at place to place on the way. Finally, after ten days of trotting and of running and of walking, at an average speed of thirty miles a day, he had reached his goal; spurred on by that agonizing kick in the ribs and by his master's bellowed command.

The ordeal had been too much for Schwartz. He obeyed orders. But it killed him. Peace to his loyal soul! For I am quite certain Schwartz had a soul; whether or not the professor was endowed with one of those annoying adjuncts.

The Alabama dog that traveled four hundred and fifty miles to his former master; the Ohio dog which journeyed three hundred-odd miles to an old home; the California dog faring all the way from near the Colorado border to Iowa—these and a horde of other authentic instances of the kind, which I have omitted because of their sameness of detail—what do they prove?

They show that a few dogs out of many have the

mystic gift of finding their way home from far places.

And we call it superhuman. It is not.

If a canine brain could function clearly, what would dogs think of our own ability to scrawl something on a sheet of paper which is readable on the other side of the world? Of our ability to unlock and then open and then close an aperture which to the dog is an oblong in an impenetrable wall?

To him it must seem incredibly magical.

But—well, a robin flies northward from somewhere in Florida every spring. If it is not killed by some pothunter during the Northward trek, it continues its unerring course, by bee-line, until it perches triumphant on the same Sunnybank veranda nook where it built its last season's nest.

That, to me, is a major miracle, compared with a dog's rudimentary homing instinct. But so common is the occurrence that nobody stops to marvel at it.

CHAPTER III

The Dogs of Kings

A CAT may look at a king. So may a dog.

Dogs are luckier than are we. When they chance to find themselves the property of some red-faced little pottle-fronted chap with a squeaky voice and a squint in his one good eye, they can judge him for what he is. Not for his rank.

To them, he is what God made him; whether for good or for bad, for grand or for rotten, for insignificant or for magnetic.

To us humans he is "George Gregorius Casimir Stefanski Stuart Habsburg, by the grace of God and of his subjects Hereditary King of Barataria and Emperor of the Forty-seven Isles."

That is where dogs have the advantage of hinged-kneed bipeds like you and me. They see only the *man*. You and I see only the *king*.

I am going to tell you in this chapter some more or less entertaining anecdotes of monarchs' dogs—of dogs which saw those monarchs only as men, not as God's vicegerents on earth. Get the idea?

Suppose we start mildly with a gray-Vandyked rotund sovereign who had a genius for the right clothes at the right time and for the right dogs at any and all times. He was Albert Edward, Prince of Wales. Afterward—*long* afterward—he was Edward VII, King of Great Britain and Ireland and Emperor of India.

For more than a half century of his earthly life he was bullied and "back seat driven" by his great little

EDWARD VII'S TERRIER
CAESAR

German-blooded mother—a genius in her way—Queen Victoria. After her death, Edward VII reigned for a sorrowfully short space of time as one of the kindest and wisest and most tactful and best-loved sovereigns in Great Britain's recent history.

And from the heart out he was an inspired dogman. For example:

The monarch's last favorite dog was Cæsar, the wire-haired fox terrier. The terrier worshiped his royal master. But at times Cæsar made life a horror for everyone else in the palace. He was direfully spoiled, and he took undue advantage of the fact that he was the king's chum.

Well did Cæsar know he was immune from punishment, whatever he might choose to do. He made the most of that immunity. His temper was sharp. His teeth were sharper. He put both teeth and temper into instant action against anyone and everyone who happened to offend him. Against everyone but King Edward himself. Cæsar looked on his king as his personal god, to be adored and obeyed and guarded.

He had his own special chairs, in various rooms of Buckingham Palace—chairs in which he alone sat or in which he was wont to curl down for a nap. Woe to the unwary guest or servant who might be so absent-minded as to lay hands on one of these chairs when Cæsar was in the room!

The king sent for Herbert Asquith, the prime minister, for an important informal conference. Asquith—pompous, austere and dressed with meticulous care—came into the study where his sovereign awaited him. Outside, the hot summer sun was shining with a glare that had dazzled the prime minister's eyes. The study was cool and half dark.

At Edward's gesture Asquith groped his way in the twilit room to the nearest chair. With stately dignity and a murmured word of thanks, he lowered himself into it.

With no dignity at all and with a mouthful of screeched blasphemy sizzling from his usually prim lips, he sprang high in air, his fingers gripping the seat of his trousers—or where the seat of his immaculate trousers had been when he started to sit down.

By sad mischance the prime minister had happened to seat himself in a chair which Cæsar long ago had pre-empted for his own—a chair on whose cool leather upholstery the little dog was dozing away the hot afternoon. Through the fiery terrier's somnolence a double insult blazed its way:

Not only was some unauthorized man trying to occupy his favorite study chair, but that shameless outlander was adding tenfold to the affront by sitting down heavily and painfully upon the sacrosanct Cæsar himself! Small wonder the spitfire dog went at once into sharply punitive action.

His needle-keen teeth met in the nearest and most biteable portion of the intruder's anatomy. As his victim leaped shriekingly upward, the seat of his trousers remained between Cæsar's rending jaws: a trophy of victory.

The king strove to keep his own face straight as he came to his exalted visitor's rescue. Sharply he rebuked the terrier—which, with true dog instinct, realized there was no punch and no real displeasure behind his master's perfunctory scolding—and fervidly he apologized to the outraged prime minister.

But the story was too good for the merry monarch to keep to himself. He told it, in strict confidence, to some friends. In less than a week it was all over England. London rocked with laughter. Asquith, to the end of his days, never was to hear the last of it. Thus could a small dog make ridiculous a great statesman.

King Edward was elderly when Cæsar was born. So

the monarch lay dying while Cæsar was in his prime. When the sovereign's last hour drew near and the journalistic death watch was set outside the palace, and the throng of renowned and useless specialists swarmed to the royal bedside to consult over the fated illustrious personage and to issue flatulent bulletins to the outer world, Cæsar was lying on guard at the foot of his loved master's deathbed.

"Toss him out!" commanded one titled physician.

The rest of the dolorous crew of doctors nodded or muttered unanimous assent. Their mumble and the sense of their mandate of exile pierced the mists which were beginning to crowd about the dying king's brain. Edward raised his head and commanded firmly:

"No. Leave him alone. Cæsar, I suppose you and I must do as we're told to, and keep warm and quiet indoors here. I'll rest a bit, as you gentlemen say I have to. But Cæsar is to stay here with me. Remember that, please. *Cæsar stays with me.*"

It was the last imperial order issued by Albert Edward, King of Great Britain and Ireland, Emperor of India. As such, it must be obeyed as rigorously as were the laws of the Medes and the Persians in Holy Writ. So Cæsar was allowed to crouch by the royal bedside as death drew near and nearer to his master.

After the end came, on May 6, 1910, an echo of the final command still remained in the hearts of those who had heard it.

For when King Edward's funeral procession passed through the streets on its way to the sovereign's burial, Cæsar marched heartbrokenly behind the royal coffin.

A few years afterward, I was toastmaster at one of

the annual banquets of the Adventurers' Club. At my right, in the place of honor, sat a tall and handsome man whose name I did not catch when we were introduced. He said some pleasant things about books of mine; and he spoke also of an article I had written not long before, about Cæsar.

"The little beggar and I had a lot of jolly walks and romps together," said he, "the last time I was at Sandringham to visit my aunt. You painted a fine word picture of him."

I decided his aunt was a caretaker or an assistant housekeeper at that former official residence of the Prince of Wales, and that the man at my right had been entrusted with the chore of giving the bereaved Cæsar his daily exercise during the royal family's absence.

After the dinner I made inquiries. I found the tall young man was Prince Aage of Denmark, royal soldier of fortune and nephew of the Dowager Queen Alexandra of Great Britain. It was Queen Alexandra to whom he had referred carelessly as "my aunt."

It was she who had taken charge of Cæsar after her son, King George V, had moved into Buckingham Palace on the death of his far greater sire; and after King George's own pet dog, Happy, had routed Cæsar out of the terrier's long pre-eminence as "The King's Friend." The queen dowager had taken the dethroned Cæsar to Sandringham with her to live out in peace what were left of his days.

Edward VII came honestly by his fondness for dogs. His mother, Queen Victoria, was a renowned dog fancier. On her visits to Balmoral Castle in Scotland she learned to appreciate and to love a breed of dog which up to then had been little known or cared for in England, though it had been honored for centuries in the Scottish highlands.

This was the collie.

Back to Windsor, from a stay at Balmoral, the queen brought in fast succession two Scotch collies, Lily and Sharp. I don't know what became of Lily. But Sharp was his mistress' comrade and adorer for a number of years. More than one of the queen's portraits includes the pampered collie. He is even depicted as sitting in lordly dignity beside his sovereign's throne.

Like Cæsar, Sharp had a temperamental, not to say cranky, disposition. He was spoiled and pampered by the queen. When Victoria crossed the English Channel for a state visit to Napoleon III, Emperor of the French (and to the super-adventurer's super-adventuress empress, Eugénie), she missed Sharp so acutely that the emperor had a secret mission sent to Windsor to bring the collie to Paris.

It has been claimed that his tactful action in this instance did more than anything else to cement the friendship between the rulers of Great Britain and France at this somewhat critical moment in continental politics.

King Louis XVI of France owned a gem of a little spaniel, Thisbe by name. His queen, Marie Antoinette, took a desperate liking to the dog, and besought her husband to give it to her.

Louis XVI has come down to us in sentimentalized history as something of a martyr. He was much more of a fat-headed fool, with a strong admixture of brute in his nature. He was far less royal at heart in some ways than were any of his costly dogs. For the first years of his married life he was dully indifferent to his lovely wife. During all of his stormy reign he was deaf to the counsels of his wisest advisers.

Sycophantic nobles and crafty politicians were forever showering him with rich gifts. The value of most of these he had not the intelligence to understand.

A miniature dog of Marie Antoinette's lost its way and rambled into the king's private garden, at Versailles, at a moment when the dull-eyed monarch was pottering glumly through the garden's paths. Louis lifted his cane in a fit of brutish crankiness and brought it down with all his might upon the little creature's back. Its spine smashed, the toy dog howled and writhed its life out amid the lines of formal flowering plants.

The queen, we read, was furious at her pet's wanton killing. By way of restitution the three-quarter-wit king gave Thisbe to her.

Thus began a chumship which death alone was able to end. (If indeed death really ended it. Judge for yourselves.)

Not long afterward the first stages of the French Revolution set in. Louis XVI and Marie Antoinette were dethroned and were cast into prison. Louis's fat head was sliced off by the guillotine, in January of 1793. Marie Antoinette was thrust into the Conciergerie, where she was allowed to live about nine months longer before she shared her husband's fate.

Thisbe, the toy spaniel, followed her royal mistress to the Conciergerie. As she sought to creep into the prison, close at Marie Antoinette's heels, a revolutionary guard kicked the pampered little dog, howling, into the crowded street outside the gates.

This was almost as needlessly brutal treatment as the quasi-sainted Louis XVI's cane had inflicted on the dog whose back he had broken. But Thisbe was not too badly hurt to creep back to the gates of the Conciergerie. There she began a long and piteous period of waiting for the return of her mistress.

Thisbe had known only the very softest side of life. She had been petted and cosseted and fed and groomed by loyal expert hands since she was born. Now she must sleep in the gutter, in summer heat or in snow and in chilly winds. She must find her food in the offal of the streets. In place of the slavish attentions paid to her by the royal servants were the kicks of the turnkeys and the cruel teasing of the Paris ragamuffins.

But Thisbe endured it all, for the sake of staying as close as possible to the prison doorway through which her queenly mistress had disappeared. A stanch little dog, if ever there was one!

A few kindly people began to talk of Thisbe's dumb devotion to Queen Marie Antoinette. The story spread. Folk came to gaze in amusement or in pity at the deserted canine chum of royalty. One or two onlookers tossed food furtively—not openly, of course, lest they incur suspicion of harboring royalist sympathies.

When her royal mistress was carried to the guillotine in October of 1793, Thisbe seemed to know what had befallen the fated queen and that her own long vigil was at an end. No longer was there any sense in her hanging around the grim iron gates of the Conciergerie. There was nobody left there to wait for. Her first master, the king, had died months ago. And now the queen was gone.

Thisbe trotted out onto the end of one of the quais which border the river Seine. There, for hours, she howled in raucous misery. It was a death wail to her master and her mistress. It was a dirge to fallen royalty, and to a dead royal regime. From every side the Parisians crowded to listen to it.

In the midst of the loudest and most ear-piercing quaver—the one unrebuked lament, that day, in Paris, for the death of a king and a queen and to the end of a dynasty—Thisbe leaped down into the swollen yellow river.

There, as she lay unresisting, the current sucked her under and drowned her.

Peace to a good little dog that had too much loyalty and too little common sense not to cast her lot with predestined losers!

Henry III, King of France, was a degenerate wastrel. If ever a man merited killing, on the grounds of general all-round worthlessness, it was he. (And presently that was what he got.)

He was a freak, in more senses than one. Among other oddities of his career he was the third of four royal brothers to sit on the French throne. His eldest

THE DOGS OF KINGS

brother, King Francis II, first husband of Mary Queen of Scotland, died childless. So did his next elder brother, King Charles IX. Neither of them had amounted to anything. But both were paragons compared to Henry.

He won his only fame as a dog fancier. He shrank the sturdy hunting spaniel into a tiny and temperamental lap dog, so small he carried always two or three or more of these toy spaniels in a jeweled basket hung about his own royal neck.

While each successive generation of Henry's dogs was scientifically bred into lesser size than its parents, yet the gallant spaniel heart and the wise spaniel brain were not bred out of any of them.

From the throng of miniature dogs the king chose three as his special pets. He named them Mimi, and Liline and Titi.

Their whole-souled devotion to their decadent master is proof of the old maxim that no man can sink too low to win the loyalty of some dog. Of the tiny trio, Liline was the wisest and stanchest. She had a queer psychic twist to her nature, too. As presently you shall see.

The three spaniels spent every hour of the day as close to the king as they could. At night they lay on guard just inside the threshold of his room. And they took their guard duty very seriously.

At the first far-off stranger footfall they were on their feet, sounding the alarm and showing their sharp teeth. None but an accredited courtier or servant could come, unchallenged, within hearing distance of the royal bedchamber. Henry declared his spaniels were his only unselfish friends in all the glittering court. Probably he was right.

Also he had superstitious faith in their powers of intuition. He shunned folk whom the dogs disliked. If he had had the sense to stick to this silly superstition and to be guided by it, he might well have lived on, to die of old age. And all later French history would have been different.

The one time he disregarded it was when Jacques Clement, a fanatic, sought an audience with him.

Even before Clement was admitted to the audience chamber, Liline leaped to the ground from her place in the basket. Snarling in mad fury, she galloped toward the door through which the visitor was to enter.

As Clement reached the threshold, Liline hurled herself bodily at him. The king shouted to her to come back. For once, Liline disobeyed him. She continued to tear away at any part of Clement's body she could reach.

At Henry's command, a courtier picked up the frantic dog. He carried her, while she writhed and snarled in helpless rage, into another room, slamming the door shut.

Vainly the toy spaniel leaped against the door's panels. She screamed at the top of her lungs, as if trying to send thus a warning to the master whose danger she scented.

And Henry? Why did he allow Jacques Clement to approach him and to kneel at his feet, when his own psychic dog chum had just shown so violently that the intruder was not to be trusted? Never before had he flouted Liline's mystic intuition. And never before had

THE DOGS OF KINGS 65

the spaniel shown such mad hatred toward anyone as to this latest visitor.

Yet the king had ordered the dog away—and, incidentally, he had ordered away his one chance of staying alive.

Clement knelt at the king's feet. With his right hand he proffered humbly a petition he had brought. Henry reached forward to accept it from him. With his left hand Clement drove a knife deep into the monarch's abdomen.

In a few hours Henry III was dead. As he died childless, the throne went to his cousin, the renowned "Henry of Navarre," whose brilliant reign changed completely the destinies of France and—to a great extent—those of Europe.

All because the frenzied warnings of one sample-sized lapdog had been allowed to go unheeded!

If you are interested in more or less farfetched coincidences, here is another:

King Henry VIII of England had a disagreement with the papal authority which at that time was dominant in his realm. In a mutual effort to smooth out the difficulty, an embassy was sent by Henry to Rome. And the membership of that embassy was too large by one. That one was a dog.

The dog was a spaniel which had belonged to the king and which Henry had in turn given to Lord Wiltshire.

Wiltshire was at the head of the embassy sent to Rome. Being fond of his spaniel's comradeship, he took the dog along.

The Pope welcomed the ambassadors graciously, as they were ushered into his presence at the Vatican. Lord Wiltshire led the delegation forward toward the papal chair, where sat His Holiness.

It was an established act of homage that such official visitors should advance to the chair and that there they should kneel and kiss the Pope's toe. His Holiness thrust forward his bared foot, according to custom, for the kiss of homage.

Wiltshire understood the meaning of the gesture. Lord Wiltshire's vigilant dog did not.

Evidently thinking that this stranger was about to kick his beloved master in the face, the spaniel darted forward and buried his teeth in the papal toe.

This deed of hideous sacrilege was the signal for a wildly riotous scene. The papal guard hacked the dog to pieces. The nerves and the tempers and the diplomatic relationship of both factions had been strained already wellnigh to the breaking point. The unfortunate biting of the Pope's great toe and the slaying of the biter completed the parley's failure. What had been planned for a politic and conciliatory conference broke up in fiery discord.

Back to Henry VIII went Wiltshire in black anger; his delicate mission botched and wrecked by a dog.

The king's own ready ire flamed up at the supposed ill-treatment his ambassadors had received at the Vatican. He severed relations with Rome. And the Church of England was created. A fairly big day's work for one master-defending spaniel!

Fox's *Book of Martyrs* describes at much length

the mishap at Rome, and in quaint diction. I am going to quote a small part of this account:

"Howbeit, one thing is not to be omitted as a prognosticate of our separation from the see of Rome: A spaniel of the Earl of Wiltshire, which came out of England with him, stood directly between the earl and the Bishop" (Pope) "of Rome when the said Bishop advanced forth his foot to be kissed.

"The spaniel went forthwith to the Bishop's foot, and not only kissed the same, unmannerly, but, as some plainly reported and affirmed, did take fast with his mouth the great toe, so that in haste he pulled in his glorious foot from the spaniel. Whereat, our men smiled in their sleeves. What they thought, God knoweth."

While we are on the theme of royal spaniels, let us waste a handful of words on those of Charles II, King of England; history's only monarch to give his name to any breed of dog. The black-and-tan toy spaniels which swarmed over England in a wave of fashion and of popular favor at the time of his reign were named "King Charles Spaniels" in his honor.

Charles's first spaniel after his coronation was named Cupid, and was known, to court and to country, as "the dog the king loves." That distinction was not on the free list. For thieves decided a king would be willing to pay goodly rewards for the return of so cherished an animal, in case it should stray from the palace.

Cupid began to disappear from Whitehall at frequent intervals. He was a fine source of revenue to many a petty crook. After one such disappearance a proclamation was sent forth from the palace; an appeal said to have been written by the Merry Monarch himself after a day when he had been besieged by a rabble of greedy office seekers; "place beggars," as they were known. The proclamation bristled with barbed stings. Here is some of it:

"It is His Majesty's own dog. Doubtless it was stolen. For the dog was not born nor bred in England and therefore would never forsake his master." (You will remember that the king's father, Charles I, had been forsaken by his English subjects and had been beheaded by them.) "Whoever finds him may acquaint him at Whitehall. Will they never leave off robbing His Majesty? The dog's place, though better than some imagine, is the only place which nobody affords to beg."

The intermittent stealing of Cupid may not have been a safe pastime for the thieves. For the spaniel's teeth were keen and ready. He was an earnest biter, on any and all occasions.

As he nestled at his master's side in the royal coach, during Charles's daily drives, Cupid seemed to regard the coach and the king alike as objects for his defending. Nobody could lay a finger on the vehicle without the dog's flying at him.

It is said the Earl of Rochester forgot this trait of Cupid's one day when the coach came to a halt just outside the Whitehall palace. Stepping forward to pay his respects to his sovereign, Rochester laid his hand on the edge of the coach's open window. Cupid nipped his fingers to the bone.

Thus the earl's speech of greeting was divided into two parts: the first spoken before, and the second part after, Cupid's attack. As a result the sentence took this form:

"God bless your Majesty—and God damn your Majesty's cur!"

Richard II, King of England, was a pretty poor specimen of man and of monarch. For which in due time, like Charles I, he was dethroned. His favorite comrade for several years was his hound, Mathe. According to Froissart, the hound shared his royal master's fortunes, good and ill, right faithfully—up to a certain point.

When Richard's banished cousin, Henry of Lancaster, came back to England at the head of an army and kicked Richard off the throne and into prison, Mathe went eagerly to captivity with the former king. There he guarded and sought to console Richard, for weeks. In fact, until the day when the victorious Henry paid his fallen cousin a visit of state.

Never had Henry of Lancaster seen Mathe until then. And the hound did not take to strangers, as a rule. Yet the moment he set eyes on Henry, the brute rushed up to him, tail wagging, and licked the visitor's hands and feet. Richard spoke to the dog. Mathe, for the first time in his life, paid no attention to the call of his master. He continued to fawn upon Henry. Richard said sadly:

"Cousin, this is a good omen for you, but a bitter omen for me. The greyhound welcomes you as king of England. Therefore I pray you to take him with you when you go. For he will follow you and forsake me."

Henry, like Richard, believed in omens. He whistled to Mathe to follow him when he went away. The dog obeyed the summons eagerly. Thenceforth he ignored Richard and devoted his whole future to the worship of Henry.

I don't believe in kicking dogs. There are better ways for us humans to show our inferiority to them. But I should have relished a chance to kick Mathe.

Many a time and in many a form the story of Frederick the Great's giant hound, Gengisk, has been told. The tale, basically, is true. But there are several variations as to its details. Gengisk was Frederick's comrade, not only at home but during military campaigns.

One night, during Prussia's war against the Russians, the king was riding alone, well within the lines. He heard something galloping behind him, and turned to see Gengisk. The hound had escaped from the royal tent and had followed his master's track.

Frederick could see the dog was tremendously excited; much more so than the reunion with the king would have warranted. He jumped up and tugged at the rider's boot, as if trying to drag him to the ground. Then he sprang at the horse's rein and then at its nostrils.

He was wildly eager to check the king's progress. For at last he planted himself in front of the steed, in mid-road, and would not let it take so much as another step forward.

Frederick knew the ways of a dog. Also he knew

Gengisk's zealous devotion to him. He guessed that something was amiss; that there was good reason why his hound should want him to halt and to dismount. Instead of ordering Gengisk aside and riding on, he obeyed the fierce pantomimic demand.

And thus once more a dog shifted the current of history.

The hound ceased to rush around the horse or to pull at his master's boot. He stood stock-still, facing the direction in which Frederick had been riding. Then he glanced worriedly at the king and resumed his attitude of listening. It was as though he were begging the monarch also to listen.

Again Frederick obeyed his hound's mute plea. For a few moments he heard nothing. Then, faintly in the distance, he caught the muffled thud of many horses' hoofs. They were moving toward him, swiftly yet with a semblance of stealth. The horses were not on the stony road, but on the wayside grass.

The king knew a detachment of his own cavalrymen would not ride in that stealthy fashion on their way home to the Prussian camp. He turned loose his mount, a slap on the flank sending the horse cantering back to the stables.

Then, with Gengisk, Frederick crawled under a culvert. Almost directly afterward a raiding party of Cossacks crossed the bridge above his head. But for the hound's warning, the king might readily have ridden up to them and fallen captive to his Russian foes.

How had the dog known the danger? Unsolvable Mystery No. 100,000 in canine nature!

Soon afterward the enemy general, Nadasti, captured a part of the Prussian camp. Frederick was not taken, but his great dog was. Gengisk achieved the dignity, so rare among his race, of becoming officially a prisoner of war. This to the delight of the enemy and to Frederick's keen grief.

When the war ended, a little later, Frederick insisted that one of the peace treaty's prime clauses should provide for the immediate freedom of Gengisk and for his restoration to his unhappy master.

I have read that the iron-hard Frederick threw his arms about the hound when presently they were reunited, and that he wept uncontrollably for sheer joy.

During Gengisk's imprisonment a small and spunky terrier had been allowed to take his place in the king's companionship, though never in the king's heart. When the big hound was brought back to the Prussian army headquarters on the bank of the Danube, the terrier resented his presence. He teased and pestered Gengisk unmercifully.

For a while Gengisk endured patiently the ceaseless torment. But one day as he was strolling along the river's edge with Frederick, the terrier nipped him once too often.

Gravely, Gengisk stooped down and picked up the wriggling nuisance by the nape of the neck. Gravely he carried him down into the water and swam toward the farther bank. Holding the terrier's head high above the surface, he made his way across the wide expanse of water.

The Danube was in flood. A lesser dog would not have dared or would not have been able to swim its full width. But the buffeting of the torrential current and the frequent impact with floating logs did not bother the mighty Gengisk.

He reached the opposite side of the river and climbed its steep bank. At the top he set the gasping terrier gently on the ground. Then the hound sprang into the river again, and swam back to where his royal master stood watching in astonishment the exploit of his dog comrade.

The terrier could not possibly swim to headquarters. He had neither the pluck nor the strength. Shame, too, may have played its part in his failure to find the nearest bridge; shame and perhaps terror. For never again did he return to camp. Henceforth, Gengisk ruled there, supreme and unteased.

The Prussian wars were over—for the usual brief space of time. Frederick had gone to his palace of Sans Souci, the palace he had decorated according to his own ideas of a place of rest and recreation and study; a place where he could entertain and argue with the literary men of France and elsewhere who were his invited and honored guests.

With him went Gengisk.

The stiffly dignified courtiers—bristling with Prussian etiquette and dull formality—stared in scandalized horror at the rough romps staged by the king with Gengisk in the prim rooms and corridors. They could not understand why their king nursed the hound through two long illnesses, tending him day and night and refusing to leave a single detail of the nursing to any veterinary or servant.

Bavaria sent a cabinet minister to Sans Souci to confer with the king on important state matters. The minister's report to the Bavarian premier began with these words:

"I found his Majesty, Frederick, King of Prussia, sitting on the floor of the throne room, feeding his large dog with beef bones from a tin basin."

When Gengisk died Frederick buried him in the center of the loveliest of the Sans Souci rose gardens. Above his dead pal he erected a splendid granite-and-marble monument. The warrior-king paid thus his last tribute to the hound which had been his best friend for so many years and which often had saved him from capture and from possible death.

Good old Gengisk! I should have liked to have him as a friend. Frederick the Great is to me more of a flesh-and-blood man and less of a stuffy statue; because of the grand hound he loved and which loved and served him so well.

Robert Bruce (or Robert *the* Bruce, as he was known in his lifetime) was Scotland's king and is forever a hereditary hero of his native land. I hate to smear a shining portrait. But Bruce seems to have been a most unconscionable ruffian. This from the actual annals of his contemporaries.

He ripped Scotland free at last from English rule. Between times he gained much pleasure from hunting with his—and other Scotsmen's—dogs. On one of these hunts he and his best hounds met defeat in their quest of a certain so-called "white" deer—probably an albino. Bruce declared the white deer was a demon in disguise. This because his vaunted royal hounds could not overtake and pull it down.

THE DOGS OF KINGS 75

In desperation, he asked if any of his followers had hounds which could overhaul and kill the mystic white deer. From the foremost of the cringing group came the reply that no mortal hounds could hope to succeed where those of the illustrious monarch had failed.

But one William St Claire, an obscure nobleman, said loudly that his brace of hounds, Help and Hold, could do the trick.

In much indignation Robert the Bruce bade him name the terms of a wager that his hounds could win in a chase where the Scottish king's best dogs had scored such a signal failure. In a spirit of bullying, Bruce offered to bet "all Pentland forest and all Pentland moor and all Pentland hills" against St Claire's head, on the result. Calmly St Claire accepted the murderous bet. And the conditions of the contest were laid out by a contingent of sportsmen.

On the day appointed for the chase, huntsmen reported the white deer was feeding in a certain copse. The hounds, Help and Hold, were brought forth from their kennels. St Claire knelt and prayed for their success—and perhaps that his own jeoparded head might remain in its wonted place on his shoulders.

In the midst of the fervent prayer, St Claire's attendants saw the white deer flit like a ghost across the nearer hills. They loosed Help and Hold. Over crag and dale the two valiant hounds chased their snowy prey. Never before in the annals of Scottish sport had there been such a run. Bruce and a thousand knights and nobles galloped in its wake.

At last the white deer was seen heading for a river. If once it could swim across that and to safety, the wager would be lost; and Sir William's head would be forfeit. Scant chance for mercy had St Claire from his bloodthirstily mean sovereign.

At the very brink of the river, one of the hounds caught the white deer by the haunch, the other by the pulsing throat. There they downed and killed the albino, by the water's edge.

To his credit, Bruce abode by the terms of the wager. We read:

"The king ... embraced Sir William and gave him those lands in free forestrie."

At the foot of St Claire's effigy, in the chapel at Rosslyn, are carved images of the hounds which laid the foundations of his family fortunes.

Robert the Bruce had another clever hound, which could track him from any distance. This dog was stolen by Bruce's mortal enemy, John of Lorne. Lorne planned to make use of the dog's strange power of scenting his royal master's steps.

Bruce and a fellow ruffian, Kirkpatrick, went in lawless pursuit of a Highland noble named Comyn—nicknamed "The Red Comyn." They followed him to the door of a church to which Comyn had fled for sanctuary. Bruce entered the church. There he found Comyn, with his arms around the High Altar. Bruce, half scared of committing sacrilege, but much more than half eager to kill his victim, stabbed Comyn once or twice, then ran out. In the church porch he met Kirkpatrick, and sobbed cravenly:

"Oh, Kirkpatrick, I misdoubt me I have slain the Red Comyn."

THE DOGS OF KINGS

"You *'misdoubt'* ye?" sneered the ferocious Kirkpatrick. *"I* mak' sikker [*I* make sure.]!"

So he strode into the sacred edifice. There with his dagger he cut off Comyn's head. From that day, the Kirkpatrick coat of arms has been adorned (or disfigured) by the motto: *"I mak' sikker!"*

The arm of the clansmen's law was set upon the trail of the kingly slayer of Comyn. Bruce fled with much haste. Lorne, his foe, set the hound on his trail. The dog caught Bruce's scent. Fast he followed the king and the latter's half-dozen guards. Until an arrow, sped by an archer of the fugitive's companions, pierced the dog's fearless heart.

CHAPTER IV

Professional Mourners

ONCE IN AN AZURE MOON a dog dies for grief at his master's death. Olaf's hound, Vigi, says *The Heimskringla*, was such a one. And every now and then the newspapers record a like case. But it is rare; vastly more infrequent than the sensational grievings of canine professional mourners.

These professionals are an interesting lot. Some of them—like Greyfriars Bobby—have won immortality in literature and in art. Most of them have scored front-page mention. I think I have worked out their reason for perpetual mourning. I can't prove my theory, but I believe I am on the right track.

At any rate, the class is large enough and famous enough and interesting enough to rate a chapter of this book of yours and mine. I shall cite only two or three incidents. They are typical of nearly all the rest. And, leading from trumps, shall we begin with the foremost of them? With the aforenamed Greyfriars Bobby?

Many years ago I went for the first of numerous times to the ancient Greyfriars churchyard in the older hillside section of Edinburgh. The spot was sacred to the memory of the Scotch Covenanters. I went there because I was planning a book which was to include some Covenanter history.

But I stopped, long before I reached the part of the cemetery associated with those worthies. Indeed I made my first halt before I entered the churchyard itself. For there, close to the gate, was the statue of a little shabby and shaggy dog of dubious breed. The statue's base was a drinking fountain for animals.

Here was the Greyfriars Bobby memorial, erected by Baroness Burdett-Coutts in honor of the churchyard's best-known and best-loved occupant. Its hero's effigy adorned the top of the low shaft. A supply of cold fresh water was at the foot of it, for the happiness of thirsty and hot and tired street dogs.

Then I went in search of the little grave with the rose tree above it, hard by the grim wall of the church itself; the grave where moulder the bones of Greyfriars Bobby and of his shepherd master. Somehow, I found this kind of quest more interesting, just then, than a Covenanter hunt.

Here is the true story of the queer little nondescript dog—a story that has been told in print at least fifty times, and usually in great deal better form than you are going to hear it told now:

One Gray, a Midlothian farmer, died in 1858. His body was taken in a cart to Edinburgh for burial. Under the cart trotted heartbrokenly a hairy wisp of a dog, probably more Skye terrier than any other known breed. He was Bobby, the dead farmer's pal and helper.

Bobby slunk alongside the coffin; head and tail adroop, whining softly to himself, as it was carried from the cart to the new-open grave in a humble part of the cemetery. He crouched, looking down at it, as it was lowered and as the sods were shoveled onto it.

Then he lay at the edge of the fresh-heaped mound of earth. As the few other mourners turned away, one of them whistled to the dog to follow. Bobby paid no heed. He lay there, his shaggy head between his shaggy paws, his brimming dark eyes fixed mournfully on the grave. There the mourners left him, thinking perhaps that he would follow them to his dead master's farm. But he did not follow them.

He lay moveless: sole guard and companion to the man who had been his god; the man whom all others now had forsaken. A cold and rainy night was drawing on. Bobby was drenched by lashes of rain and whipped by the blasts of icy wind. But discomfort and a wetting and chill and hunger had not the power to make him forsake his self-chosen post.

Through the long cold night he lay on guard. There in the morning the church's sexton, James Brown, discovered his presence. The cemetery rules were strict. Brown prided himself on obeying them. One of these rules read:

"No Dogs Shall Be Admitted."

This little bedraggled and shivering nondescript terrier had, it seems, admitted himself to the sacred precincts, and actually was lying beside a new grave. In prim horror at such desecration, James Brown drove Bobby out into the street, aiming kicks and stones and wrathful names at him, as the poor little chap scuttled away, frightened, into the downpour of rain and into an alien city.

That evening at dusk, Brown was making his final rounds of the cemetery. Through the wet twilight he could see the wretched Bobby, soaked to the skin and trembling all over. The dog had found his way back to his master's grave. Once more he was pitifully on guard there.

That morning, Brown had supposed Bobby was merely some stray cur that had wandered by chance into the churchyard and had curled up there for a nap. Now he saw him again, huddled against the same new grave. That was not the deed of a chance wanderer. So he forbore to drive him out.

Just then one of the grave diggers chanced to go past, on his way home. He recognized Bobby as the dog who had followed the coffin and had stared down so mournfully at it as it was heaped high with earth. He told Brown the tale.

Gently, this time, the sexton bade the dog begone, hoping to make the wretched little starving beast go home where he could find food and shelter. But Bobby turned a deaf ear to the persuasive voice.

Brown let him stay where he was. He did more: From his pocket he exhumed a hunk of bread left over from his own noonday meal and tossed it to the famished little fellow.

Bobby swallowed it at a single gulp, for he had eaten nothing for nearly two days. He tried to wag his stumpy tail in gratitude. Then he huddled again close to the mound. And there Brown left him to his inclement vigil.

That night at Trail's alehouse at the lower end of the "wynds" the sexton told his story to a group of fellow tipplers gathered around the peat fire of the taproom. He depicted in booze-inspired pathos the loyalty of the farmer's terrier in doing voluntary guard duty above the remains of his owner.

He told the tale well; and dramatically. It caught the ale-warmed fancy of his fellow tipplers. Among these were a sergeant and two or three private soldiers from the castle barracks. Present, too, was a hungry young scribbler for an Edinburgh newspaper. Trail, the fat landlord, deigned to listen.

Yes, the sexton had a varied and appreciative audience as he stretched his lean shanks to the glow of the peat fire that cold night, with his pint mug balanced on one horny palm. He expounded ever more pathetically and graphically upon the subject of Bobby's fidelity. And his narrative had a big and immediate effect on the terrier's future. For example:

Trail promised to provide the shaggy dog with a full meal of table scraps every day thereafter. The sergeant guaranteed to Bobby, henceforth and for life, a big raw beefsteak once every week. Most important of all, the reporter hustled back to his newspaper office, the liquor still actuating him to fluent sentiment, and wrote a sob-sister saga of Bobby's fidelity.

That was the beginning. And it was plenty. Like Byron, Bobby next day "awoke to find himself famous."

People crowded to the churchyard to gaze on him and to bring him gifts of food; and presently to erect above his frowsy head a watertight canopy to keep out the rain and snow, and to put on the ground beneath it a thick, warm mat for him to lie on.

PROFESSIONAL MOURNERS 83

Innkeeper Trail showed Bobby the way to his alehouse and trained him to come thither precisely at noon every day for a heaping plateful of scraps. The sergeant brought him, weekly, his big chunk of raw steak.

In short, the erstwhile tramp dog was all at once living in luxury. And he was the focus of thousands of admiring eyes. Tourists from as far away as London, and later from the United States, journeyed to Edinburgh to see him; as one newspaper and magazine article after another blazoned forth his queer fame.

He had a comfortable bed. He had a snug shelter from the sun and snow and rain. He had more food than any three hungry dogs could have gulped down. Most inspiring of all, he ha dthe openeyed admiration of daily hordes of visitors. What more could a vain little Skye terrier ask for? Despite his vigil's sadness, Bobby reveled in it all.

When he had finished his daily visit to Trail's alehouse and his round of the neighborhood, always he trotted back to his master's grave and resumed guard duty in his very comfortable living quarters there.

The all-powerful Edinburgh *Scotsman* not only printed his story, but started an inquiry which resulted in finding whose dog he had been; as well as his name and his earlier history. Henceforth he was known as "Greyfriars Bobby."

The law took a hand in the game, and declared Bobby was a stray and that he must be treated as such; unless some reputable townsman would go bond for his good behavior and would guarantee his yearly license fee. A hundred volunteers clamored for the honor. But Trail was ahead of all the rest.

The mayor—or lord provost—of Edinburgh formally presented him with an ornate collar whose price had been raised by eager subscription. Gourley Steele, renowned animal painter, made a strikingly lifelike portrait of him. Copies of this were sold everywhere. I have one of them. Other artists sketched or painted Bobby.

Thus, in such comfort and high repute and adulation as seldom has befallen any mortal dog, Bobby continued his vigil, year after year. Never did the public weary of him. Never did it cease to stare and to admire.

On the morning of January 14, 1872, Bobby was found lying dead—of the maladies of overripe and overfed old age—in his snug canopied bed alongside his master's grave.

For nearly fourteen years he had been a public character, a local hero. And nobody knew how old he had been when his owner died. Edinburgh mourned loudly the loss of its best-known citizen, its foremost drawing card for the tourist trade.

Now, at first glance, this is a right pathetic and tear-squeezing yarn.

To me, it is nothing of the kind.

I think Bobby had fourteen years crammed full of comforts and vanity and happiness. He had a better time than even the most pampered lapdog. I can't find it in my callous heart to join in the universal chorus of pity for him.

Mind you, I don't doubt, for an instant, that he had

PROFESSIONAL MOURNERS

been devoted to his dead master. I am certain Bobby's heartbroken devotion was 100 per cent genuine on the day when first he stretched himself out on the ground in the pelting rain by the grave. I admit all that. *But*——

Except for the doubtful blessing of speech, there is less basic difference between some dogs and most small children than you may realize. Let a human child be admired, praised, rewarded, for some unintentional witticism or Smart Alec stunt. What happens? The child will keep on duplicating and repeating those words or that exploit as long as the chorus of admiration can be made to continue.

Take Greyfriars Bobby: Almost at once he found he could command an applauding audience and much good food and an exceedingly comfortable abode; and that this continued and increased as time went on.

How had he attracted all this popularity and publicity and all these delicious victuals? By moping disconsolately beside a grave. Was it not dog nature—would it not have been child nature, or even average adult nature—to continue the stunt which brought in all this flood of desirable things?

One of my own Sunnybank collies—Sunnybank Sandstorm (Sandy) was praised and patted when, as a puppy, he picked up his brimming feed dish and carried it carefully to where we and several guests were sitting, and deposited it at my feet. He was mightily pleased with himself.

To this day, nearly twelve years later, whenever there are guests at Sunnybank at his feeding hour, crippled old Sandy picks up his laden dish and brings it to me. Always he does it with the self-consciously proud air of one who performs a brilliantly amusing trick. (And always the crippled and half-blind old collie is praised and rewarded for the silly action as vehemently as if he had saved a child from drowning. Which is sloppy of us, I admit without argument. But the old have so few thrills! And Sandy is cruelly and painfully old.)

Again, at St Pierre-et-Miquelon, one summer not long ago, a Newfoundland bitch was hailed as a heroine when she sprang into the sea from a pier and swam ashore with a baby who had tumbled off the stringpiece. The Newfoundland was the resort's petted and overfed darling for the next week. Then she had to be shut into her kennel yard until the tourist season was at an end.

This because she insisted on giving dozens of encore performances by butting unwary children off the end of the piers into deep water, and then plunging into the ocean to tow them ashore.

Now perhaps you may see why I discount the sincerity of Greyfriars Bobby's grief during the best part of his fourteen years' vigil, and why I include him among canine "*professional* mourners."

Perhaps I am mistaken. But I think not. And I think you may agree with me when (and if) you read the story which is to wind up this chapter's anecdotes. But there are other stories before then, all of them seeming to bear out my cynical theory. For instance:

Here is the tale of a professional mourner whose

PROFESSIONAL MOURNERS 87

devotion has been celebrated in verse, both by Sir Walter Scott and by Wordsworth.

Charles Gough, an Oxford student, early in the nineteenth century, planned to spend the Easter vacation on a walking trip through the Westmoreland and Cumberland mountains, with the peak of the much-touted Helvellyn as the goal of his hike. With him he took his terrier, a dog which had shared his collegiate life.

More than once Gough had been fined by the college authorities because the terrier had worked its way out of its quarters in a stable and had tracked its master to the "No Dogs Allowed" precincts of his room.

It was whole-souledly devoted to the youth.

During the walking tour, Gough and his dog stopped for awhile at an inn in Paterdale. Then they started to climb Helvellyn's crest and thence to descend to Grassmere on the mountain's far side.

Blithely they set forth.

Weeks later, inquiries were made for the missing collegian. He and his terrier never had arrived at Grassmere. Search was made. No results. Months crawled by.

Then a shepherd scoured Helvellyn for a lost sheep too big for the mountain-summit's eagles to have carried away. At a lonely gorge amid the rocks he heard a bark. It was a high-pitched yapping; not the challenge call of one of the region's collies. The shepherd investigated.

On an outjutting ledge of rock crouched Gough's terrier. The dog seemed sleek and in good condition. Perhaps the lost sheep or newborn lambs of its race might have had something to do with the guardian dog's plumpness and air of contentment. At any rate, it seemed proud of its long period of watchfulness over Charles Gough's dead body which lay sprawled in front of it.

Subsequent praise and wondering stares and zestful offers of adoption apparently were a joy to the professionally faithful beast. Fidelity or exhibitionism?

In Paris, 1830, there was a revolution which sent King Charles X sprinting from his throne and from the city, in quest of safety. The monarch fled. Some of his loyal adherents stayed on and fought uselessly at the impromptu barricades.

These were mowed down most mercilessly. Then the bodies of the dead were hauled rudely into the gardens and lawns of the Louvre. There they were spread out on the grass.

The public at large was told it might come into the palace grounds and look at the lines of corpses, with an idea of identifying and claiming any friends who might be among them.

In swarmed the rabble; some genuinely in search of missing relatives or comrades, some drawn by morbid curiosity.

As the crowd tramped amid the rows of slain, their mutters of prurient excitement were broken in upon by a savage growl. From above one of the bodies arose a dog: gaunt, fierce, terrifying, alertly on guard.

He had been lying vigilantly across the body of his lifeless master, a young Parisian rioter who had fallen at the first volley of the national guard.

PROFESSIONAL MOURNERS

Evidently the dog had followed him to the street barricade where he was shot, and later had trailed his body to the Louvre gardens; and had found and mounted guard above the corpse. There he had crouched, fierce and alert, ever since.

His sad loyalty to the dead man caught the fancy of the public. Through Paris ran the story. It lost no flesh at each retelling. Folk brought every type of food, from lamb cutlets to broiled chicken, to the gallant mongrel. They stood in circles around him and told him how splendid he was.

Do you wonder the watchful brute began to give himself airs; that he learned to pick and choose from among the hundredweights of provisions that were laid in front of him; to be friendly with some of his fatuous admirers and snappily cranky with others?

Until now he had lived on gutter crusts and on such sparse and lowly fare as his rioter master could give him. But suddenly he had stopped being a kicked street cur and had become the pampered idol of Paris.

In the newspapers and in the broadsheet prints he was acclaimed as "The Dog of the Louvre."

He was Paris' unofficial ward and pet. About him clung an air of drama and of tragedy and of deathless fidelity. It went to his head. He continued to loll on the spot in the gardens where his master had been laid—though that master long since had been taken away and buried—and to receive the plaudits and the masses of indigestible food forced on him by his unending throng of daily visitors.

At the end of three months an indiscriminate diet and wholesale gluttony and a dearth of exercise did their fell work. The Dog of the Louvre died from an orgy of overeating. He was mourned by the whole sentimental city.

One more case of canine vanity? Or death from heartbreak for a lost master? The former, I think. Blighted creatures don't gorge all the food in sight, nor fawn on some visitors and snap and snarl at others.

Dr J. E. Harry, in his exhaustive volume, writes thus of the Louvre mourner's daily bill of fare:

"People came from far and near to see him, and gave him their bread, their meat. Children gave him the cakes their mothers had bought for them."

Do you wonder the Dog of the Louvre succumbed to indigestion—not to grief—after all Paris had been stuffing him with tons of indigestible food for months?

Let's get down to a more recent instance of a canine professional mourner; to Buster, a farm collie whose sad story has been printed and reprinted in fifty newspapers during the past few years.

Buster started out as a very genuine mourner for the master who had trained and cherished him. Bit by bit he slipped into the position of part-time mourner. He and his photograph (in mourning pose) were familiar figures to newspaper readers, from time to time, over a rather long stretch of years. Here is the true yarn:

He was a farm collie. He belonged to James S. Van Court, of Richmond, Ohio. For seven years he was his master's chum; and he won fame as the best herder and driver and watchdog and all-round canine farm worker in the county. Among other things, he was taught in puppyhood the precise boundaries of Van Court's land and that he never must set foot beyond those boundaries. (That is learned by many country-bred dogs, and it is a decidedly necessary accomplishment.)

When Buster was seven, Van Court died. The Richmond cemetery was on a hill, some little distance from the farm. The collie had lain at his master's bedside throughout the last illness and until the body was coffined.

As neighbors carried the casket across the fields and up the hill to the graveyard, Buster followed dejectedly until he reached the boundary of the farm. There he came to a stop. All his busy life he had known he must not go beyond that border line.

Obedience and habit were strong upon him, even on this black day of heartbreak.

But something else was stronger; something which seemed to force him to follow his human god to the end of the road, no matter how many hard-binding sacred commandments might be smashed in the process. So after a few seconds of worried hesitation he sprang forward, and caught up with the slow-moving procession.

Close behind the coffin he paced, until the grave was reached. There he stood, as had Greyfriars Bobby, until the earth was mounded and the last mourner went away. Then he lay down on the heap of fresh sod.

Softly Mrs Van Court had called to him to come home with her. Next to his master the dog loved his master's wife better than all else. Ever he had been gaily obedient to her least word or gesture. But today the summons fell on deaf ears. Buster would not stir from the grave, nor so much as glance back at his mistress.

The cemetery superintendent came with his men to brush the loose dirt from the plot and to clear up the place after the funeral. They saw Buster lying disconsolately on the grave. They called and chirped to him. There he lay. The superintendent put a hand on the wontedly gentle dog's collar, to draw him forcibly away.

There was a snarl, then a flash of teeth. The man backed off, nursing a slash on the wrist. Buster spent that night on his master's grave.

By the next day the story had spread. Presently it reached the newspapers. Here was a pippin of a human-interest yarn. The cameramen and the reporters flocked to the grave. So did neighbors and more distant sightseers.

There lay Buster, mourning the owner he loved. Athwart Van Court's mound he crouched, baring his teeth at anyone or everyone, except Mrs Van Court, who might venture near. To Mrs Van Court he was noncombative. But he would not come home, at her coaxing, nor pay any heed at all to her. The rest of the visitors found him an excellent dog to stay away from.

Food and water were brought to the grave. Folk cooed and crooned at him and praised him. If ever you have owned a typical collie, you will understand what this flattering attention did to the grieving dog's vanity and how it established him in his role of professional mourner.

The vigil which had begun in bitter heartbreak began to assume the more salient features of a party. Here were quantities of rich food, here were a horde of humans making much of him and sympathizing with him. Apparently Buster grew to thrill to it all.

Yet he ate little and drank less, and he lost weight. His untended coat grew muddy and matted and stringy. At these increasing signs of pining away, human attention redoubled. In scorching suns, in sluicing rains, Buster maintained his queer vigil; while the farm work suffered acutely from the chore dog's absence.

But all novelties become shopworn. In a month or two the newspapermen and the sightseers and the rest of the gratifyingly sympathetic onlookers had stared their fill at the collie who was starving himself to death on Van Court's grave. It had been an enthralling sight. But there were other things to see and to do, and in many other places.

Attendance dropped off at the grave. It dwindled to practically nothing. Buster was left alone to his pitiful guardianship of the dead. By this time, he himself was all but a skeleton, and he appeared almost too weak to get to his feet.

Yet here is what the famished and feeble collie did:

Early one morning, he left the grave. He galloped (galloped, not crawled weakly) down the hill to the farmhouse. There he greeted delightedly the Van

Courts; who were incredulous in their joy at seeing him there again. He ate an enormous breakfast and he drank at the pump tub for several minutes.

Then he flashed down to the barnyard and to the milking shed, first pushing up the latch of the byre gate and letting it swing open. He rounded up the cows, drove them skillfully through the gateway and herded them along the road toward their pasturage.

Arrived at the pasture he nosed open its gate; as he had been trained to do, long years before. He bunched the cattle and sent them into the pasture. Then he shoved shut the gate behind them till its latch clicked.

Back to the farm he loped. There he continued with the rest of his former chores. Snappily and smartly he went through his lifelong duties; ending the workday by going to the pasture and bringing home the cows to the milking shed.

After which, sombrely and dolefully, he climbed the cemetery hill and laid himself down with a sigh on his master's grave. There he spent the night, returning to his feed dish and his farm work early next morning. You see, Buster had become a *part*-time mourner.

The news of this latest phase ran through the region and to the newspaper offices. It caused a recrudescence of interest in Buster. It brought batches of visitors once more to the cemetery.

And Buster did not disappoint these new admirers. Almost every day, whenever he could spare an hour or two from his farm duties, he would trot up to the churchyard, lie disconsolately on Van Court's grave and indulge in a brief mourn; while men and women and children eyed him in gratifying pity.

Every night, even after this fresh influx of spectators had stopped coming thither in bulk, the collie would climb the hill from farmhouse to cemetery, and spend the night on the grave.

Always he took the same route, the way trodden by the mourners who had carried Van Court's coffin up the hill. In time the dog's padding feet wore a deep groove in the hillside grass, from his more-than-once-a-day progress up and down the same track.

This for another eight years.

Then, at fifteen, age began to take its cruel toll of the collie's once-tireless strength.

Rheumatism gnawed at his joints and muscles. He waxed fat with the unwieldy flesh of canine senescence. His dark eyes were bleared.

Yet every evening, in all weathers, Buster toiled painfully up the slope which once he had traveled with complete ease. Nightly, he exposed his rheumatic old bones to rain or cold or snow, in order to sleep where so long he had slept. In vain the Van Courts sought to dissuade him from the quixotic double journey.

Age battled with determination. And, as ever, age won. Many of us humans live too long. But I think all dogs die too soon.

On a spring night in 1936, Mrs Van Court was awakened by a sound as of soft sobbing on the side porch just beneath her bedroom window. She found Buster lying on the doormat, moaning to himself. He had tried for the last time to mount the hill to the cemetery. His strength had given out. His ancient sinews had disobeyed the command of the ageless will power.

So, crestfallen, the exhausted old dog had crawled back to the porch mat where he had slept, every night, during his master's lifetime. Helpless to move further, he had stretched himself out on the floor, whimpering weakly at his loss of power.

As Mrs Van Court bent tenderly above him with words of friendliness and comfort, Buster called on his wornout body and his will for one last supreme effort. He wagged feebly his plumed tail, and he lifted his head and licked the woman's hand.

Then he slumped back, stone dead.

Van Court's grave was at the edge of the hill cemetery, close to the boundary fence. Van Court's sons dug a grave for Buster at the outer edge of the fence, as near as possible to the spot where his long-dead master slept.

Peace to Buster's loyal soul—and to what I am so cynical as to regard as his genius for showmanship!

I am going to end this chapter with one more tale of a four-legged professional mourner; one of the most ludicrous dog stories I know. I was going to save it for my chapter on Freak Dogs. But I append it here for the sake of proving my contention that the average professionally mourning dog is "putting on an act."

Here is the true story, as it appeared, bristling with photos, in fifty newspapers a few years ago:

In Minneapolis there was a widow, very rich, very

old, very lonely. She lived in a big house and she was tended by a mob of upper and lower servants. She had no relatives nearer than a half score of distant cousins.

Her real name would not add to the strength of this anecdote. So I am going to put spurs to my imagination and invent a quaint oriental nickname for her. Let's call her "Mrs Smith."

Well, Mrs Smith died, in the fullness of years and in her palace of a house. And friends and acquaintances and hangers-on and distant cousins and more dubious relatives turned out in wholesale numbers to attend her funeral.

Toward the cemetery the pompous burial cortege wound its impressive way. Apart from the gloomily impressive hearse and the open cars bristling with rich floral tributes, twisted an endless line of motors filled with those who had come to pay their last respects to her. But directly behind the hearse—in front of the flower-choked open cars and the cars conveying the troop of cousins—walked a dog.

He was a collie, big and black and funereal of aspect. Head and tail down and with misery in every line of his splendid body, he plodded somberly at the heels of the hearse.

Every paper next day commented sloppily on the death-defying devotion of Mrs Smith's favorite dog.

As the procession trailed its glum way to the ornate family plot of the Smiths, the black collie left his place close behind the hearse. He moved over to the edge of the gaping grave. There he stood during the ceremonies.

When the last spadeful of earth had been tossed

decorously into the cavity, he lifted his pointed nose to the skies and howled in ear-splitting dolor. Then he sank to the ground, across the mound, trembling and groaning. There he lay.

When the undertaker's men tried to dislodge him, he snapped and snarled. When the procession had departed, he stayed on. Some attendants threw scraps of food to him from their dinner pails. This repast he ate willingly enough. But he showed his teeth in evil menace when anyone dared come within a yard of him.

There he remained.

Now let's save time and wordage and stupid repetition by saying that all the features of the professional mourning of Greyfriars Bobby and of the Dog of the Louvre and of Buster were repeated with almost no variations.

The public heard the tale of the pitiful vigil. They came to sympathize and to stare and to feed. The newspapers played up the pathetic story in grand shape, with gallons of sobs. The press cameramen wasted plate after plate in picturing the black and broken mourner.

The distant cousins of Mrs Smith came forward, stung by certain newspaper comments. They said they would be only too glad to give a good home to the loved and loving pet collie of their deceased relative. They vied for the honor. So did other kindhearted newspaper readers.

Then came an element of bewilderment. Mrs Smith's servants and her secretary and her nearest friends testified unanimously that the deceased woman never had owned any kind of a dog, to say nothing of a lanky black collie, and that she had had no interest whatever in dogs.

This added mystery to pathos. There was a deadlock. The deadlock was broken by a young man who lived in a suburb some miles from Minneapolis. He took one sharp look at the group of photographs in the local papers. Then he exclaimed joyously:

"Why, that's *Jack!*"

Some days earlier, the youth had driven to Minneapolis on business. He had taken along his big collie, the dog he had bred and had owned and cherished since Jack's birth.

He went into an office building, leaving Jack outside, as often he had done.

But this time the collie strayed or was stolen. When his owner came out of the building his dog was nowhere to be found. In vain he advertised. For days he searched the city for him.

When he saw the newspaper photographs, he drove straight to the cemetery. There lay the funereal black dog, with a swarm of admirers around him. The youth called:

"Jack! *Jack,* you old fool! *Come here!*"

With a yelp of delight, the collie bounced up from his solemn resting place. He burst through the ring of spectators, and ran to his owner.

Squealing and wriggling with rapture at the reunion, he preceded the man to the car and hopped into it; wagging his tail and pawing his master in ecstasy, and with never a single backward glance at the grave where he had lain so long and so unhappily.

The most normal solution I can offer for this silly

story is that Jack was wandering about confusedly in search of his lost master when he chanced to see the funeral procession of Mrs Smith. Collies are queerly responsive to any form of human emotion. Sensing the general air of lugubrious decorum, the dog had fitted himself to that mood. And he had dropped into line directly behind the hearse.

When he found his wholly normal action in lying down wearily for a rest atop the comfortable soft pile of earth was the cause of so much flattering attention and of so much food, he decided to stay there and to resent all efforts to dislodge him.

At last he heard the voice of the master he had lost and had been seeking so vainly. Whereat Jack's period of professional mourning ended with much abruptness.

Once more he became in a trice a normal and fun-loving and master-following collie. His season of simulated grief was past.

CHAPTER V

Some Sunnybank Dogs

A SCHOOLTEACHER, looking back over his experiences with more than a thousand pupils, would find himself dwelling with special interest in recollections of at least nine or ten of them; nine or ten personalities so outstanding, for one reason or another, that they will not let themselves be forgotten or grouped with the vast majority.

It is so with my memories of the long line of Sunnybank dogs. (Skip this chapter, if you aren't interested in such rambling personal sketches.)

Soon or late, every dog master's memory becomes a graveyard; peopled by wistful little furry ghosts that creep back unbidden, at times, to a semblance of their olden lives. To outsiders, the past deeds and misdeeds of these loved canine wraiths may hold no great interest.

With this somewhat windy apology, which really is no apology at all, let's go:

Lad stands out as foremost of the dogs of Sunnybank. I have written his life saga; stretching its exploits through no fewer than three "Lad" books. So I need not go in for a wearisome retelling of his biography. A few episodes and characteristics, and then we'll pass on to the next cage.

He was a big and incredibly powerful collie, with a massive coat of burnished mahogany-and-snow and with absurdly small forepaws (which he spent at least an hour a day in washing) and with deepset dark eyes that seemed to have a soul behind them. So much for the outer dog. For the inner: he had a heart that did not know the meaning of fear or of disloyalty or of meanness.

But it was his personality, apart from all these things, which made—and still makes—him so impossible to forget. As I have tried clumsily to bring out in my three books about him.

He was immeasurably more than a professionally loyal and heroic collie. He had the most elfin sense of fun and the most humanlike reasoning powers I have found in any dog.

Suppose we talk about those traits for a minute or two.

The Mistress and I went to pay a call of sympathy on a lachrymose old woman whose arm had been broken. The fracture had knit. The victim was almost as well as ever. But she reveled in giving dramatic recitals of her mishap to anyone and everyone who would listen.

We took Lad along with us when we dropped in on the invalid-emeritus. Before we had been there five minutes, we had every reason to wish we had left him at home.

Not that he failed to behave with entire outward decorum. But he took much uncalled-for part in the conversation. The woman launched forth on a detailed report of her accident. She sprinkled the lamentable recital thickly with moans and groans and belching sighs.

Lad was enormously pleased with the performance. So much so that he elected to turn the dolorous solo into a still more doleful duet. Every time our hostess gave forth one of the many successive sounds of grief, Lad copied it with startling realism and in precisely the same key. In perfect imitation, he moaned and whimpered and sighed and emitted ghastly groanings.

Throughout, he was lying demurely at the Mistress's feet. But his eyes were a-dance. The plumed tip of his tail twitched uncontrollably. Lad was having a beautiful time. The Mistress and I were not.

We sought to keep our faces straight, as the woman's narrative waxed in noisy intensity and as Lad's accompaniment swelled to a crescendo.

Groan for groan he gave her and moan for moan. Carried away by his own brilliant enactment, his ululations increased in volume until they all but drowned out the sufferer's performance. It was a horrible duel of emotional expression. And Lad won it. For the woman paused in her jeremiad, and stared down at the statuesquely couchant collie in tearful admiration.

"Oh, he's wonderful!" she exclaimed. "Just *wonderful!* He understands all the agonies I've been through! And it almost breaks his heart. I wish some people were half as sympathetic as this poor dumb beast."

Lad, who for five minutes had been anything but dumb, eyed her in happy expectation; waiting for her to strike the next imitable note of grief, and yearning for a chance to resume his own performance. But there was no opening. The lament had shifted to clamorous praise of the dog's unbelievable comprehension and sympathy. And in the hymn of praise there were no alluring groans to copy.

We got away as soon as we could. If ever a dog merited rebuke for disgraceful impudence, Lad was that dog. But neither the Mistress nor myself had the heart to scold him for it.

With uncanny wisdom the collie had realized from the outset that the old lady was in no pain, in no real distress, that she was just airing her past trouble in maudlin quest for sympathy and in an orgy of self-pity. And he had joined blithely in the scene; in a spirit of straight ridicule.

In cases of genuine human distress or pain or misfortune, Lad's sympathy was ever eager and heartsick. But he had a whole-souled disgust for any form of faking; a disgust he took pleasure in showing most unmistakably.

Sometimes his guying took a subtler form. As when a man came here to see me on business—a man Lad disliked and distrusted as much as did I. The day was hot. The visitor took off his new pongee coat and laid it on the edge of the veranda. Then he began to talk.

He had an unpleasant manner and he was saying unpleasant things. I was hard put to it to remember I was his host, and to behave civilly to him. I found the effort more and more difficult as the talk went on.

Lad was lying beside my chair. As always, he sensed my mood.

With a collie's odd psychic powers he knew I was increasingly angry and that I yearned to kick the visitor off my land. The dog looked worriedly up into my face. Then he eyed my caller, and the tip of one of his long white eyeteeth peeped from under the lip that had begun to curl ever so slightly.

I could see the tiger muscles go taut beneath Lad's coat. I laid my hand on his head and whispered sharply:

"*Quiet,* Lad. Let him *alone!*"

All his adult life the dog had known the meaning of both those commands and the stark necessity of obeying them. Yet the Master was pestered by this obnoxious stranger. And, with Lad, that was not on the free list. Glumly he lay down, his eyes fixed alertly on the guest.

Then, stealthily, he got to his feet. With catlike softness of foot he crossed to the veranda edge where was draped the visitor's imported white coat—a garment of much value, even if not of many colors. To my shame I admit I saw the collie's progress without checking it. I had used up my whole day's stock of hospitality.

Lad lifted the snowy and costly coat from its place. He carried it out onto the muddy gravel of the driveway as tenderly as though it were a sick puppy. The owner was too busy orating to notice the rape of the garment. And I had not the good breeding to call Lad back.

On the driveway, Lad sought out a spot where was a smear of surface mud and silt as wide as a dining-room table—the effluvia of that morning's heavy rain.

With the same exaggerated tenderness he laid the coat atop the area of mud. Then, in very evident relish, he proceeded to roll on it, back and forth, several times. After which he proceeded to rub one of his heavy shoulders into the muddily crumpled British imported pongee, and then the other shoulder. He ended the desecration by rolling once more upon it.

Now to an outsider this shoulder rubbing and rolling might have had no significance, apart from crass mischief. A dogman would have understood the unspeakable black insult implied. For only into carrion—liquescent and putrescent carrion—does a dog roll and rub his body in that fashion. It is the foulest affront he can offer.

It was when Lad had completed his task of defilement as I have told it and was pacing back in majestic dignity to his place beside my chair, that the visitor's eye chanced to rest—first inquisitively and then in swift horror—upon his treasured white coat; or at the befouled bunch of muddy cloth which had been that coat.

Again I should have reprimanded Lad right ferociously. Again I did not.

In October of 1912 the Mistress was stricken with a long and perilous attack of pneumonia. It was a time of horror which even yet I don't like to recall. Through the endless days and the interminable nights Lad crouched against the door of her sickroom. He would not eat. If he were put out of the house, he would smash a cellar window, and, two minutes later, he would be back at his post outside the shut door.

Day and night he lay there, shivering, moaning

LAD HAD COMPLETED HIS TASK OF DEFILEMENT

SOME SUNNYBANK DOGS

softly under his breath. Doctor and nurse, coming or going, would tread accidentally on his sensitive body a dozen times a day.

Outside, the October woods were full of chaseable rabbits and squirrels: Lad's lifelong pacemakers in wild-forest chases. But the dog paid no heed. Miserable and sick with dread, he lay there.

Then, of a glorious Sunday morning, the death danger was past. I called Lad into the sickroom. Trembling, ecstatic, he made his way to the side of the bed, moving as softly as any nurse or mother. The Mistress was told of his long vigil. And she patted his classic head and told him what a grand dog he was.

Then I told him to go outdoors. He obeyed.

Once outside, he proceeded to comport himself in a manner unworthy of a three-months puppy.

For the next ten hours complaints came pouring in on me: complaints ranging from tearful to blasphemous; complaints I was too happy to heed.

Lad had broken into the dairy, by hammering open its door with his head. There he had pulled, one by one, every milk or cream pan from the shelves, and had left the stone floor deep in a white covering.

Lad had chased the Mistress's cat up a tree. And the poor little feline was stranded out on the end of a wabbly bough whence only a long ladder could rescue her.

Lad had gushed forth among the cows and had driven them into stampede flight. One of them, tethered to a long chain, he had chased in a circle till the chasee was too exhausted to stand.

Lad had cantered up to the gate lodge. There he had slipped into the kitchen and had yanked from the open oven a ten-pound leg of mutton designed for the Sunday dinner of my superintendent and his family. This hotly savory trophy he had been burying deep in a flowerbed when the superintendent's wife rescued it in sorry plight.

Lad had nipped the heels of an elderly horse which drew a carryall wherein his owner and the latter's children were driving to church. The horse had run away, more in conscientiousness than in terror, for several yards, before the driver could rein him in.

Meantime, Lad had sprung upward and had caught between his teeth the corner of an elaborate laprobe. He had dragged this for a quarter mile, and at last had deposited it in the dead center of a half-impenetrable berry patch.

Lad had hunted up three neighbors' dogs and had routed them out of their kennels and had bestowed on them a series of terrific thrashings.

Lad had ripped the nurse's best newly starched uniform from the clothesline (he hated the antiseptic-smelling and abhorredly efficient nurse from the first) and had deposited it in the black lakeside mud.

In brief, Lad had misbehaved as never before in all his stately life had he dreamed of misbehaving. He had been, for ten hours, a Scourge, a neighborhood Pest.

Fast and furious poured in the complaints from everywhere. To my lasting discredit, I must say I made the same reply to every weeping or cursing complainant:

"Let him alone. Send me the bill and I'll settle it. Lad and I have been through the red flames of hell, this past fortnight. Today he's doing the things *I'd* do if I had the nerve. We're celebrating, he and I."

(I don't need to point out to any of you that this was an inanely drunken speech for any grown man to keep on repeating as I repeated it on that golden Day of Deliverance.)

A year later, Lad took upon himself, of his own accord, a man's size job. Namely, the task of shaping his harum-scarum young son, Wolf, into a decent canine citizen. Patiently, the big dog wrought at this chore. At first the results were slow and uncertain.

For one thing, Wolf's inborn sense of mischief made his sedate sire's life a burden. The worst form of plaguing was the stealing by Wolf of Lad's most cherished meat bones.

At first the older collie suffered these thefts without resentment or punishment. Lad could thrash (and *did* thrash) every dog of his size, or much larger, which attacked him. But against a silly half-grown pup he would not employ his fearsome punitive powers. He hit on a better trick for keeping his beloved bones from Wolf's thieving teeth. I was lucky enough to be on hand, at a distance, to see this ruse carried out more than once. And, to me, it savors, not of blind atavistic canine instinct, but of true human sense of reasoning.

Lad received, as part of his dinner, a gorgeously meatful beef bone. He had eaten to repletion. Thus he planned to bury this delicious two-pound morsel for future exhuming and gnawing. First, he took preliminary steps.

Then with no show of caution at all he carried the red-streaked bone to a sheltered spot in a flower border. There he laid it down and proceeded to dig a hole in the soft loam—a hole deeper than he usually dug.

In the bottom of this pit he placed the bone. With his nose, he shoved an inch or so of earth atop the buried treasure. (A dog digs holes with his fore paws, you know. But he uses his nose, never his paws, for filling such holes. I don't know why.)

After the bone was comfortably if lightly covered, Lad dived into a clump of shrubbery hard by, and reappeared carrying a bare and sterile bone he had hidden there—a bone which long ago had lost its last iota of dog appeal and which had been bleached white by many rains.

This forlorn relic he dropped into the cavity. Then he proceeded to push back all the displaced dirt, up to the level of the rest of the ground; and walked unconcernedly away, not once turning to glance back at the cache.

Wolf had been watching from a safe distance, and with avid interest. As soon as Lad left the scene of interment, the puppy danced over to it and began to dig. Thus, often, he had rifled his sire's underground bone-repositories. Presently, Wolf had dug down to the first bone.

In disgust he sniffed at its meatless aridity. Then he turned away. Apparently he had had all his toil for nothing, for less than nothing, for a bone a starving coyote would have turned up its nose at. Off trotted the baffled puppy without the faintest suspicion that a right toothsome meat-fringed bone was lying less than two inches beneath the decoy bone he had disinterred.

Now, unless I am more in error than usual, that ruse of old Lad's called for something like human reasoning and powers of logic. Assuredly it was not based on mere instinct. Every move was thought out and executed in crafty sequence.

I have heard of two other dogs, since then, whose owners saw them do the same thing.

Let's go back to an aftermath of Lad's crazy spree of relief when he knew the Mistress was out of danger. A week or so later, the convalescent was carried downstairs, one Indian summer morning, and ensconced in a porch hammock. Lad, as always, lay on the veranda floor beside her.

During the forenoon, two or three neighbors came to see the Mistress, to congratulate her on her recovery and to bring her gifts of flowers and candy and fruit and the like. These presents they placed in her lap for inspection. Lad watched interestedly. Soon he got up and loped away toward the woods.

Somewhere far back in the forests he found—much more likely *re*found—the carcass of an excessively dead horse. From it he wrenched part of a rib. Then, dragging his heavy burden, he made his way home.

None of us noticed the collie's approach; the wind blowing from the wrong direction. Our first knowledge of his return to the porch was when he came alongside the hammock and dropped his awful gift across the Mistress' lap.

And why not? To a dog, such far-gone carrion is a rare delicacy. Not for food, but to roll in. To him the odor must seem delicious, if one may judge by his joy in transferring it to his own coat.

Lad had followed the example of the morning's visitors by bringing his dear deity a present—the choicest he could find.

After all, the reek of carrion cannot be much more offensive to us than is the smell of tobacco and of booze and of costly imported perfumes, to dogs. Yet for the incomprehensible pleasure of being near us, our dogs endure those rank smells; while we banish from the house any dog whose fur has even the faintest reek of carrion.

Of all my countless ignorances of dog nature, the densest is his yearning to be near his master or mistress.

I don't know why my collies will leave their dozing in front of the living-room hearth for the privilege of following me out into a torrent of winter rain. They hate rain.

I don't know why all folk's dogs risk gladly a scolding or a whipping by breaking out of a room or a kennel into which they have been shut, and galloping down the street or over the fields to catch up with the master who purposely has left them behind.

Today (for another and non-thrilling instance) I am writing at my hammock desk, a hundred yards or more from the house. Seven dogs are with me. It is a cool, brilliant afternoon; just the weather for a romp. The lawns and the woods and the lake all offer allurement to my collies.

What are the seven doing? Each and every one of them is lounging on the ground, close to the hammock.

Even crippled and ancient Sandy (Sunnybank Sandstorm) has left the veranda mat where he was so comfortable. To him all movement nowadays is a source of more or less keen discomfort. Yet he limped painfully down the six steps from the veranda to the driveway, and came slowly over to me, as soon as he found I was here; stretching himself at my feet, on bumpy ground much less comfortable than his porch bed. And here for the past two hours he has been drowsing with the others.

Why? *I* don't know. There must be some mysterious lure in the presence of their human gods which gives dogs that silly yearning to stay at their sides; rather than to do more amusing and interesting things.

When I chance to go from the house toward the stables, a cloud of the white doves of Sunnybank fly to meet me and to escort me in winnowing flight to my destination. There is no mystery about this semblance of devotion. They know their food box is in a shed there.

The same cause was assignable to the welcoming whinnies of my horses (when I still kept horses) that greeted me as I passed in through the stable doors in the early mornings.

It is the same with the goldfish, when a hundred of them converge in fiery streams to where I halt at the curb of the wide lily pool; and when they wriggle fearlessly in and out among my dabbling fingers. They know—or hope—I am there to feed them.

No, none of those phenomena holds a single half-grain of mystery, any more than does human fawning on a rich relative. But the dogs—mine and everyone's—stick around where we are and go where we go, through no graft motive at all.

They are absurd enough to want to be with us, and with no hope of reward. That is an impulse I have sought hard and vainly to explain to myself.

In the bunch of Sunnybank collies, as they lie around me here on the grass, there is no trace of the flattering attention they show toward the maids, who love to feed them surreptitiously from the kitchen windows; none of the still more rapt interest they bestow on my superintendent as he prepares their one ample daily meal.

There is no such patently self-seeking tinge in their attitude toward me as they lie here on the lawn. There was none of it in the canine procession which followed me to the house, three minutes ago, when I went to my study for a new supply of typewriter paper, and which waited at the door for me and then convoyed me back here to the hammock.

No, it is a trait I can't figure out. As I think I have said several times in the past page or two.

Which is a long digression from our story. I like to hope it hasn't bored you overmuch. And now let's get back to Lad:

I have dealt here only with a few of the queerly human and mischievous and logic-guided happenings in Laddie's life. Not with his actual history.

His death battle with two younger and stronger

dogs in the snow-choked forests back of Sunnybank, his deeds of dashingly worshipful service to the Mistress and to myself during his full sixteen years of life, the series of stark adventures that starred his long career—are not these chronicled to perhaps tiresome length in my three books about him?

Foremost among the Sunnybank dogs of my childhood and young boyhood was my father's oversized pointer, Shot. He is worth your notice. Naturally, in any modern dog show Shot would be "gated" most unmercifully.

He was of royally pure blood. But his head lacked the so-styled refinement of today's show pointer. His mighty chest and shoulders and hindquarters that carried him tirelessly for ten hours a day through the stiffest kinds of shooting country, and the harsh coat and thick skin which served as armor against briar and bramble and kept him unscathed through the thorniest copses—these were at laughable variance with the silken skin and dainty narrow-chested body lines of the show-type pointer of nowadays.

At "laughable" variance. But to me the laugh would not be on Shot. For, to me, he still is, in memory, the grandest pointer of my rather long experience.

My mother's health broke. My father took her and all of us to Europe, in the hope of curing her. (The cure was made. She lived more than forty healthy years longer.)

Sunnybank was rented during our two-year absence from America. Shot was sent to one of my uncles to be cared for until we should come back for him.

This uncle, Colonel G. P. Hawes, Sr, was an ideal sportsman. He understood dogs as it is given to few men to understand them. He and Shot had been good friends, since the pointer came to us as a just-weaned puppy. The dog could not have had a better home and a more congenial guardian.

Yet Colonel Hawes wrote my father that the usually gay dog had grown sullen and mopey and spiritless. Shot went through his duties in the hunting field as honestly as ever, but with no interest. He was grieving sorely for his absent master and for Sunnybank.

After our two-year exile we came back to America. One of my father's first moves was to go to my uncle's home and bring Shot to Sunnybank. He took me along on this errand. Its details are as clear in my memory as if they had occurred last month.

As soon as we were seated, Colonel Hawes sent a man to bring Shot into the house. The dog was kenneled some distance away and had not seen or scented our arrival. Into the living room plodded the pointer, at my uncle's summons.

He was thinner, much thinner, than I remembered him. His gait and his every line and motion were listless. He seemed wholly without spirit and devoid of any interest in life. My father had arranged the scene beforehand. He had told me what to do. I did it.

He and I sat motionless and without speaking. We were at the end of the room farthest from the door, and we were seated perhaps ten feet from each other.

Lifelessly, Shot came through the doorway. Just inside the threshold he halted. Up went his splendid

SOME SUNNYBANK DOGS 119

head. His eyes sought out my father's mute and moveless figure. For a second or more the dog stood so.

Then he began to creep toward my father, hesitantly, one slow step at a time, crouching low and shuddering as with ague. Never did his dazed eyes leave my father's face. Inch by inch he continued that strangely crawling advance.

He did not so much as glance toward where I was sitting. His whole mind was focussed on the unmoving and unspeaking man in the chair ahead of him. So might a human move toward the ghost of a loved one; incredulous, hypnotized, awed. Then my father spoke the one word:

"Shot!"

The dog screamed; as though he had been run over. He hurled himself on his long-lost master, sobbing and shrieking, insane with joy. Then the sedate pointer whirled around him in galloping circles, and ended the performance by dropping to my father's feet; laying his head athwart his shoe and chattering and sobbing.

I drew a shaky breath. At the sound Shot raised his head from its place of adoration.

He dashed over to me and accorded me a welcome which ordinarily would have seemed tumultuous, but which was almost indifferent, compared to the greeting he had accorded my father. Then, all at once, he was back to his master again, laying his head on the man's knee and still sobbing in that queerly human fashion.

(Yet not long ago I read a solemn scientific preach

ment to the effect that no dog could remember a lost master's face and scent for the space of eighteen months! Shot beat that record by a half a year. And I believe he could have beaten it by a decade.)

To Sunnybank we came; Shot with us. The dog's sullen apathy was gone—gone for all time. He was jubilantly happy at his return to the home of his earliest memories. But for weeks he would not willingly let my father out of his sight. He seemed to fear he would lose his master again.

My father taught me to shoot. A few years after our return to America he and I went out quail-hunting with Shot. At the base of a steep hill there was a brambly meadow. The meadow was cut midway by a railroad track. As he neared the track, the dog came to a dead point. He was facing a clump of low bushes on the far side of the rails.

Statue-still, Shot stood, at point, waiting my father's signal to move forward toward the clump. Before that signal could be spoken, an express train came whizzing around the curve at the foot of the hill, and bore down toward us. Under its wheels and in its wake was a fog of dust and of flying hot cinders.

Shot stood, rocklike, on his point. The train roared past, not ten inches from his nose. The dog did not stir or falter, though he was peppered with burning cinders and choked by the whirlwind of dust and soot.

After the train had rattled its ill-smelling length out of the way, my father signaled Shot to move forward. The pointer took two stealthy steps ahead: steps that carried him to the center of the railroad track. From the clump just in front of him three quail whirred upward like a trio of fluffy little bombs. I suppose they had been too scared by the passage of the train to break cover until then.

Shot dropped to the ground, tense and waiting. My

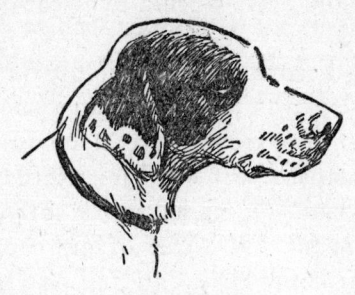

OLD SHOT

father brought down two of the birds in one of his customary brilliant left-and-right volleys.

I missed the third.

I was too shaky over the dog's peril and his plucky ignoring of it to do any creditable shooting just then. Shot lived to a ripe—an overripe—old age. We buried him in a strip of lakeside land a furlong or more from the house: a strip where sleep the Sunnybank dogs of almost eight decades. He was interred next to a grave whose little marble headstone's blurred lettering still may be deciphered as

FRANK Our Dog. For Thirteen Years
Our Faithful Friend. Died 1876.

Frank was Shot's immediate predecessor as my father's hunting companion.

Frank bit me when I was at the age of two. I had tried to bite off one of his floppy ears. It was a punitive nip Frank gave me rather than a real incision. I am told I wept loudly at the scare and hurt of it.

(If "when a man bites a dog, that's *news*," I wonder if it is tabloid news when a two-year-old boy chews a dog's ear.)

It was long before my birth that my father bought Frank. The dog was just past puppyhood. The time was winter. So my parents were at Newark, where my father was pastor of the old First Reformed Church. Not at Sunnybank. (Even as, to my sorrow, I was not born at Sunnybank like three of my nephews, but at Newark; because my birth date fell on December 21st —my mother's forty-second birthday.)

Young Frank was restless in his new home. On the day after his arrival he ran away. My father and my mother and my two elder sisters and the servants went to look for him. All in different directions.

My mother wandered about for an hour, calling the pointer's name from time to time. At last, just in front of her, in the twilight, she saw him emerge from an alleyway. She called to him. He paid no heed, but walked away. She gave chase and overhauled him. The dog showed his teeth as she grabbed him by the collar. This though he had seemed to take a genuine liking to her after his arrival at our home.

She ripped a flounce or something from an underskirt—women wore a labyrinth of underskirts and petticoats in those prehistoric days—and fastened it to his collar. Then she proceeded to drag him homeward.

"Drag" is the right word. For the pointer fought and held back every step of the way. A small but enthusiastic crowd formed, and followed the pair with shouts of gay encouragement. After a mile of hard going they reached our house, at 476 High Street.

In triumph, if in much weariness, my mother hauled the snappingly protesting dog indoors and into the firelit living room.

There, in front of the hearth, lounged my father. Frank was asleep on the rug at his feet.

The runaway dog had tired of his roamings and, half an hour earlier, had come back home of his own accord; just as my father was returning from a fruitless search for him.

The dog my mother had kidnaped was enough like him to have been Frank's twin brother. They never knew who the other pointer belonged to. But when they let him escape into the night he bounded off as with some evident destination in view. For weeks thereafter my mother dreaded arrest on a charge of dog stealing.

Never again did Frank run away, throughout the thirteen happy years of his life. Every winter he stayed on at Sunnybank when the family returned to Newark. There, in the absence of his gods, he made himself a member of the superintendent's family at the gate lodge; waiting in weary impatience for the family's return home.

When in early spring our carriage and the baggage wagon turned in at the gate, Frank would follow them down the winding furlong driveway to Sunnybank House. Here, till our departure in late autumn, he remained. And he would bark harrowingly at the superintendent or at anyone of the gate-lodge household who might venture to come near our door.

He was a peerless field dog and a peerless watchdog. To the inch, he knew the boundaries of our land. No unauthorized outsider might pass those boundaries without instant challenge and assault from Frank. He treed several innocent (if any of their foul breed can merit the term, "innocent") sightseers. He was a Neighborhood Terror.

Nightly, at stated intervals, he would leave his porch mat and would patrol the outside of the house and every part of Sunnybank's home tract. He was perhaps the best of all the great Sunnybank watchdogs we have had over a period of nearly eighty years.

I never liked him. And he didn't like me. Thus, my praise of his worth comes from my brain and from my conscience, not from my heart. He was bitterly and justly resentful, too, when in his old age young Shot came here to take his place in the field work he no longer had the strength or endurance to perform. I can't blame the ancient dog for that.

It was soon after Frank's death that someone gave my mother a miniature black-and-tan terrier. She named her "Jip," after Dora Copperfield's tiny dog. Though Jip nominally was my mother's, yet the little terrier chose my father as her only god. Her devotion to him was all-engrossing. She insisted on going everywhere with him. Sometimes this was not wholly pleasant.

As when, one Sunday, she was locked safely at home

in his study while the rest of us went to church. My father was in the midst of his sermon when Jip came strutting proudly up the aisle.

A servant had gone into the study to replenish its fire. Jip had sneaked out, unseen. Somehow she had made her way to the street. There she had had no trouble at all in picking up my father's trail and following it.

Happy at the reunion with her adored master, Jip eluded easily the grabbing hands of the sexton and of one or two of the worshipers whose pews she went past. Up the pulpit steps she bounded, and leaped to the pulpit itself, landing squarely if scramblingly on the open Bible.

My father did not so much as pause in the delivery of his sermon, nor did he heed the snickers of the congregation. Which showed fairly good self-control, I think, as he had not noticed the terrier's progress up the aisle, and as his first intimation of her presence was when she appeared, wagging her tail and wriggling with joy, on the top of the pulpit's Bible.

Without checking his discourse, my father picked up the little morsel of caninity very gently and thrust her into one of the flowing sleeves of his black clerical gown.

From that exalted position, her beady eyes surveyed the congregation in triumph. Throughout the rest of the long church service she did not stir. She just cuddled deep in the folds of her master's silken sleeve, her alert head alone visible to the grinning onlookers.

If she shamed us on that day, she more than atoned for her sin a few nights later.

Always she slept on the foot of my father's bed. He woke to hear her growling with falsetto intensity far down in her throat. Then she sprang to the floor and scampered out of the room and downstairs.

A moment later, the house re-echoed to her furious barking. My father went down to investigate. For never before had the good little dog done such a thing as to disturb the slumbers of the family. Others of the household also went downstairs to find what it was all about. As a result, a burglar was nabbed and jailed. In his cell, later, the man gave this testimony:

"The thing we're most scared of in a house is a small dog that barks and keeps backing away, like that black cur at Dominie Terhune's last night. You can't make them shut up and you can't get close enough to them to land a kick. They wake up everybody."

So much for gallant and adoring Jip. I don't remember what became of her. And now, a good deal more than a half-century later, there is nobody I can ask. Peace to her, anyhow! She stood patiently for a godless lot of mauling from my grubby childish hands. I recall that much, very distinctly.

Jock and Jean were son and mother. Both were children of my great collie, Bruce, "The Dog without a Fault"; the hero of my book that bears his name.

Usually a mother dog loses all special interest in her pups soon after she has weaned them. That was what Jean did, in regard to most of her many offspring. But never with Jock.

To the day of Jock's death he was still her cherished baby. Daily—though he grew to be almost twice her size—she would make him lie down, first on one side and then on the other, while with her untiring pink tongue she washed him from nose to tail tip.

She superintended his eating. Daintily she would transfer from her own food dish to his the choicest titbits of her dinner.

It was pretty: this love and care of the little brown collie mother for her big brown collie son. And Jock reciprocated it all to the utmost. He and Jean were wretchedly unhappy when either was forced to be away from the comradeship of the other for more than an hour at a time.

Jock was one of the best collies, from a show point, I have bred. Close he was to complete perfection. In his only dog show he cleaned up everything in his classes against strong competition; and he was beaten for "Best of Breed" only by his own peerless sire, Bruce.

This meant immeasurably less to me than did my success in breeding into him a clever and gay and courageous spirit and a flavor of wise "folksiness" which made him an ideal companion. Mentally, spiritually, in disposition, he was a replica of Bruce. I asked (and ask) better of no dog on earth. As to his jolly pluck:

From the time he could leave the brood nest, Jock feared nothing. He would tackle any peril, any adversary, with a queerly happy and defiant high-pitched bark whose duplicate I have yet to hear.

That queer bark of glad defiance was ever his war cry.

On a day, while I sat writing in my outdoor hammock, young Jock lounged at my feet. He leaped up, suddenly, with that jocund challenge bark of his.

I looked behind me. There I saw on the lawn a big and thick-girthed copperhead snake. The serpent had been gliding through the grass toward the hammock and toward my unheeding ankles, when Jock either had sighted him or else had become aware of the nauseous viperine odor—a stench as of stale cucumbers—which clings to such venomous snakes.

In some occult way, Jock had seemed to divine my possible peril. He had sprung up from his doze and had rushed at the copperhead, sounding his glad battle cry. The snake checked its own slithery advance. It coiled, and prepared itself to face this plangent new adversary.

Many a fool dog would have plunged forward to death. Many a more prudent dog would have avoided the issue. Jock was neither a fool nor prudent.

It was a new experience to me to watch his duel with the copperhead. Never before, I think, had he encountered a snake. Yet he fought with consummate skill. In and out he flashed, tempting the copperhead to strike, and then dodging back, barely an inch out of reach of the death-dealing fangs; and immediately flashing in with an effort to slay the serpent before it could coil afresh.

Each combatant was a shade too swift for the other. Back and forth for some seconds waged the death duel. Neither adversary scored the fatal bite, though more than once each was within a hairsbreadth of it. And ever rang forth that odd battle bark of my young collie.

Then I had sense enough to realize that I was allowing an untried paragon to pit his skill, for life or for death, against the most deadly type of viper in this region. And I went to his help.

I smashed the copperhead's ugly triangular skull under my heel.

This with no zest at all. For I was wearing low shoes of canvas at the time. And if I had missed, the snake might well have scored on my unprotected ankle. I had a twinge of mental nausea as I gauged the distance and the required speed and accuracy for my head blow.

(There is little of the hero and a goodly modicum of the coward in my make-up. I detest danger and all its by-products. But Jock was my chum. And he was risking life for me.)

The heel came down fatally on the fat copperhead. The fight was ended. So was the snake's life. And for two days thereafter Jock would have nothing whatever to do with me. I had spoiled his jolly life battle by butting in on it and by slaying his very entertaining opponent. He viewed me with cold aversion, until his youth and his inborn love for me overcame his disapproval.

But we were chums, he and I, for a pitifully short time after that.

For, a week later, like the fool I was, I took him to the dog show I have mentioned. He had been inoculated twice against distemper, and I used every other preventive and safeguard I knew of. (Doses of Delcreo in advance, a sponging of mouth and of pads with grain alcohol directly after the show, followed by the rubbing of flaked napthaline into his luxuriant coat and a liberal dosage of castor oil.)

But a distemper-sickening chow had touched noses with him briefly at the big show. And that was enough. Jock was the more delicate because he was so closely inbred. He was infected. Ten days afterward he developed a dry cough and a wet nose.

The disease had set in. The malady which kills more purebred dogs than do all other diseases put together; the malady which took horrible toll from that same show and which has killed more than a thousand dogs a month, in its flood tide, after other shows.

Distemper practically never kills a mongrel (crossbreed is a better term) which it assails. The afflicted dog crawls under the barn or into some other cool and dark hiding place. Thence he emerges a few days later, bone thin and weak, but cured. But it slays at least fifty per cent of the thoroughbreds it attacks. Sometimes more.

It is a disease which, like typhoid, its human counterpart, calls for twenty-four hours a day of nursing. And, as in typhoid, nursing is 90 per cent of the cure.

Not often does actual distemper kill its victims. Oftener they die of its sequel illnesses: pneumonia or pleurisy or chorea. Chorea is a form of St Vitus's dance. With dogs, almost always it is fatal.

Jock weathered the distemper itself. I nursed him, twenty-four hours a day, through the pneumonia which followed upon it. Then through the long siege of chorea which came after pneumonia. I cured him of each successive one of these scourges, though I waxed dead on my feet from sleeplessness and from eternal vigilance during every one of them.

I gave up all attempt to work. And I spent my days and my eternally long nights in the wide box stall that was Jock's sickroom. Then, just as success seemed ahead, the youngster somehow acquired "re-infection." At least that is what the two vets named it.

At gray dawn of one November morning I sat on the floor in a dim corner of the box stall, with Jock's head and shoulders pillowed on my aching knees. I had had seven weeks of the conflict, with not one night's rest. Yet I was thrilled at the idea I gradually was winning the battle for the good collie comrade I loved.

Jock had been sleeping peacefully for hours. Suddenly he lurched to his feet. His fevered eyes were fixed on something in the black shadows at the far opposite corner of the wide stall; something my own gross human gaze could not see.

Forward he sprang, voicing that same strange high challenge bark of his. Then he fell dead, across my outstretched feet.

What did he see—if anything—lurking there in the stall's far corner? Probably nothing. Perhaps "the Arch Fear in visible shape." Whatever It was, brave young Jock had no dread of It. With his olden glad bark of defiance he had staggered forward to meet It.

Perhaps some of us soul-possessing humans may die a less valiant death.

At sunrise I had my men dig a grave for Jock, far from the house, and in the center of the line of Sunnybank dogs' graves I have spoken of, at the lake edge and on the border of the more distant woods. There we buried the fearless young collie; buried him almost six feet deep, before we fumigated his box-stall sickroom.

For the past weeks Jean had been shut up in her own spacious kennel yard. That day I let her out, for the first time since her loved son had fallen ill. Eagerly, unwearyingly, the little she-collie searched every inch of the forty-acre Place. Back and forth and in narrowing circles she coursed and cast, in quest of Jock.

After several hours she came to the grave of her puppy. There she halted; first sniffing about, then waving happily her plumed tail and nestling down beside the mound of new earth.

There was nothing sad or hopeless in her attitude and aspect. It was as if, after long search, she had arrived by chance at a spot nearer her precious son than she had been for weeks.

Presently she got up and ran to find me. Then she led me joyously to the grave; and once more she snuggled down to it, with waving tail and happy, smiling eyes. There she stayed all day. Not mournfully, but in pleasant expectation.

There was no taint of exhibitionism or of the role of professional mourner, or even of grief, in her bearing. She had missed her dear son all these weeks. Now at last she was nearer to him than she had been throughout that long time of waiting. Her sense of smell told her that.

Several times before settling down there she circled the ground, nose to earth, for a radius of perhaps thirty feet, as if in search of some newer trail to follow. There was none. She realized she was closer to him, at his grave, than anywhere else. Presumably she believed Jock would come back to her, there, in course of time. So she waited, in happy eagerness.

She did not establish a senseless twenty-four-hour-a-day vigil. But every morning, as soon as she was let out of her kennel yard, she would canter to Jock's grave in that same blithe expectation of finding he had returned. There she would stand or lie for a few minutes before going back to the day's usual routine.

She was a strangely lovable little collie, was Sunnybank Jean; with a hundred pretty ways that were all her own. The Mistress, whose property she was, used to say:

"Any burglar could steal Jean if only he'd pat her while he was doing it."

Unlike most of our collies, she loved petting, even from strangers. And she delighted in the arrival of guests.

At sight or sound of a car coming down the furlong of winding wooded driveway from the highroad above, Jean would run to the foot of the drive at the veranda's edge and stand wriggling with jolly anticipation, thrusting forward one of her white fore paws in an effort to shake hands with the approaching visitors —even while their car still was many yards away.

Two minor mishaps were forever befalling Jean. One was the wedging of some fragment of bone into the hinges of her jaw at the very back of her mouth. This propped her jaws wide apart and she could not close them or get rid of the obstacle. The other was throwing her shoulder out of joint during a gallop or a romp.

Both these things happened again and again. But they did not bother her. Invariably she would come straight to me with a flatteringly trustful expression on her visage; an aspect which said as plainly as could any shouted words:

"Boss, I'm in a jam again. But it's all right, now that you're here. *You'll* fix it for me. You always do."

With plumed tail awag, she would stand patiently and even gaily while I pried loose the lump of knucklebone from between her jaw hinges, or pulled the dislocated shoulder joint back into place.

One morning, when she was let out for a run, she went as always to Jock's grave. On her way back to the house she heard a car starting down the drive from the highroad. In her role of Reception Committee, she raced to her usual place of welcome and stood with fore paw outthrust in a handshaking gesture.

The car, laden with sightseeing strangers from far away, had crashed the gates at the lodge and had sped down the drive at perhaps forty miles an hour. This with the customary sweet disregard for the several "Please Drive Slowly" signs which disfigure our trees along the way.

Perhaps the driver did not notice the beautiful little collie near the veranda; the canine Reception Committee with waving tail and politely extended fore paw, waiting so happily to welcome the newcomers.

The car went over Jean, disemboweling her and breaking most of her bones.

She must have been in hideous agony during the few

minutes before she died. But not so much as a whimper escaped her. She was as plucky as they make them.

When I ran out of the house, toward her, Jean lifted her head and turned it toward me with the same flatteringly trustful expression that always had been hers when her jaw hinge was blocked by a bone or when her shoulder was out of joint; the expression that said:

"It's all right, now that *you're* here. *You'll* fix it for me."

A large woman in bright blue was among the tourists who debarked tumultuously from the killer car. Breezing over to where I knelt beside my dead little collie friend she made graceful amends for everything by assuring me with a gay smile:

"I am really VERY sorry this has happened."

(What a heaven-sent gift it must be, to know how to say just the right thing at just the right time! Hers was a talent to be envied. Yet for the only time in my life I replied to a woman's words with a torrent of indescribably foul blasphemy.)

A local magistrate fined the head of the party one hundred dollars for trespass and for malicious mischief or for some such fault. He wanted to make the sum much larger. I persuaded him not to. I told him the mischief had not been malicious, but idiotic. Which was far worse, but not so heinous in the eyes of the law. Also that if he should fine every unwarranted sightseer motorist who trespasses on Sunnybank's posted grounds the national debt could be wiped out in no time at all.

I told him to divide the hundred dollars between

two village charities. Which he did. I wanted no part of the blood money that he imposed for my collie chum's killing.

As far as I was concerned I thought the rotten incident was closed. It was not.

A syndicated newspaper column's space, two days later, was devoted to the affair and to denouncing me venomously for my boorishness in penalizing a party of "kindly meaning hero worshippers who had traveled so far to see me." Several papers throughout the country—one of them a religious weekly—printed editorials along the same general line of invective.

Thus I lost not only good little Jean, but much popular approval and, doubtless, many readers.

I write to interminable length and perhaps with no great faculty for holding people's interest, when I get started on the subject of my Sunnybank collies. Yet in this chapter I have scratched only the surface of the theme. A hundred other loved and noteworthy dogs of Sunnybank must go unsung, Gray Dawn among them.

CHAPTER VI

Dogs of Great Authors

IN NEWSTEAD ABBEY'S GARDEN, in Nottinghamshire, England, is a pompous shaft of stone—"a little monument more neat than solemn," as its designer wrote of a much better memorial column in Rome. Under the Newstead Abbey monument the bones of a grand dog have been crumbling for more than a century. The dog was Lord Byron's immortal Newfoundland, Boatswain.

Boatswain meant more, in his day, to Byron than did anything else on earth. Together the poet and the Newfoundland roamed the Nottinghamshire woods and fields—Byron young and lame, the dog young and splendidly sound. Together they lived and wandered; throughout most of Boatswain's too-short life. Theirs was a perfect comradeship. Or as nearly perfect as Byron's eternally posing and affected and selfish nature could permit.

Newstead Abbey, by the way, was no longer an abbey, but was Byron's country place. There he and boon companions of his would dress as monks and sit around the long refectory table and fill the once consecrated rooms with obscene song and blasphemy and would wax exceeding drunk as the night wore on.

But soon or late all his guests bored and annoyed the poet. And when they were gone he would turn gratefully to Boatswain for cleaner and more normal comradeship.

His next best friend at Newstead was the ancient

BOATSWAIN
LORD BYRON'S FAMOUS DOG

butler who had served his father and his grandfather before him; almost the only man Lord Byron trusted.

One day Byron summoned the old butler, and outlined eagerly to him a morbid plan.

"I am going to build a magnificent tomb in the garden," he announced. "And beneath its shaft, when we come to die, you and I and Boatswain are to be buried, side by side."

The butler said nothing, just then, but stumped back to his pantry. Byron was cross and astonished that the old fellow should have shown so little enthusiasm over the beautifully poetic scheme.

Next day his astonishment was cleared up, even if his crossness was intensified. Glumly, the butler gave warning that he was about to leave Byron's service. The poet protested in vain. The old man was rock firm in his resolve to leave. After long questioning, the truth came out in a gush of angry words:

"I've served your lordship faithfully," sputtered the butler, "even as I served your father and his father before him. But the time has come for me to leave Newstead Abbey. And I'm leaving. If you have got to have the reason, I'll tell you, though it shames me to say it. It's that plan of yours to build a tomb where your lordship and me and the big dog here are to be buried together. That's why I'm going."

He drew another deep breath, then hurried on with his explanation:

"Dogs live only a few years at best. And Boatswain isn't any too young now. He'll die, first of the three of us. And you'll have him buried under that monument you're aiming to build. I'm past seventy. So I'll die next. And if I was still in your lordship's service at my death, you'd have me buried there alongside of Boatswain.

"Your lordship is just over twenty. Belike you may have sixty years of life ahead of you. Sixty years of life and fame. Sixty years to forget all about me and Boatswain. And when you come to die, the nation will bury you in Westminster Abbey, along with the rest of the great folks.

"Then when Judgment Day comes and all the dead shall arise from their graves, like Holy Writ says—well, me and Boatswain would pop out of the ground, close together, side by side, from the same grave. And, if I might make so free as to ask your lordship the question, what impression would Gabriel and St Peter and the rest of them, On High, get of me when they found I'd been the sort of foul wretch whose fellow men thought he was only fit to be buried along with a dog? Where would I be shipped to, then? No, your lordship. I'll be leaving here tomorrow. No Boatswain Tomb for *me!*"

It was in 1808, not very long after the butler's resignation, that poor Boatswain fell mortally ill. Byron, for once, forgot to be profoundly selfish. Night and day he nursed the dog, even though he was warned by the veterinary that the malady was rabies and that it might readily infect anyone who handled or tended the sufferer.

Byron was deaf to the danger. He himself washed out the slavering mouth and he sponged the froth from Boatswain's jaws. With no fear, he performed every needful service for the rabid brute nobody else dared to touch.

Score one good point for a man who had few enough of such points to his credit!

Afterward he wrote to one of his friends:

"Boatswain is dead. He expired in a state of madness, after suffering much, yet retaining all the gentleness of his nature to the last; never attempting to do the least injury to anyone near him. Now I have lost *everything* (except old Murray!)"

"Old Murray" was his publisher, whom Byron alternately abused and made fun of and shocked; and of whom he never missed an opportunity of saying or writing something amusing. If the poet had been as whole-souledly grief-stricken over Boatswain's death as his letter implied, I don't think he could have chosen that moment for one of his characteristic digs at his publisher.

Nor, if his grief had been so overwhelming as he pretended, do I think he could have composed the epitaph and the poem which were to adorn Boatswain's ornate tombstone. Verse and epitaph have become classics. I need only touch on a few phrases from them to refresh your memory.

The epitaph was a bitter fling at the human race's inferiority to dogs. It described Boatswain as combining "beauty without vanity, strength without insolence, courage without ferocity, and all the virtues of man without his vices. * * * This praise, which would be unmeaning flattery if inscribed over human ashes, is a just tribute to the memory of Boatswain."

The mordant poem, which also was engraved on the monument, sneered at mankind's boastful claim to be exclusively the tenants of heaven; and pointed out Boatswain's superiority to any human. It ended with this couplet which you have heard quoted many times:

To mark a friend's remains, these stones arise.
I never knew but one—and here he lies.

Boatswain seems to have been the only dog in Byron's life. This, according to the poet's own testimony. He was not a friend of dogs, *as* dogs. Indeed, he had a pretty poor opinion of them. To his boon companion, Tom Moore, Byron wrote:

"As for my canine recollections, as far as I can judge by a cur of my own (always excepting Boatswain, the dearest and, alas, the maddest of dogs!), I had one, half a wolf by the she-side, that doted on me when I was ten years old and very nearly ate me at twenty.

"He bit away the seat of my trousers, and never thereafter would he consent to any kind of recognition of me; in despite of all the bones I offered him. So let Southey blush, and Homer, too; as far as I can decide upon quadruped memories."

Yet, as part of his eternal posing, Byron had referred to himself in verse, just before writing this letter to Moore, as "friend of the dog, companion of the bear!"

Perhaps the most genuine friend of dogs, in the long roster of authors, was Sir Walter Scott—another poetic genius who, like Byron, was lame. Scott's novels, as well as Scott's life, fairly bristled with dogs; from the mighty vengeance hound in *Talisman* to the likable little waddling hairy terriers in *Guy Mannering* and in other Waverley tales.

Copies of Landseer's painting of Scott's own dogs at Abbotsford have hung on the walls of a thousand homes.

Camp stands out as foremost of these dogs—not in form or in beauty but in his master's affection. Camp was a halfbreed; part bulldog, part rat terrier. For more than twelve years he was Scott's chum.

There was a queer protectiveness on the mongrel's part toward his gigantic lame master. Again and again Camp would slow down his own fast pace to accommodate his speed to the limping giant's. As do my Sunnybank collies to my own recent lameness.

When the climbing of some stiff hillside was too much for Scott and he stopped to rest, Camp's solicitude was as affecting as it was ludicrous. The dog would leap up, whimpering, to kiss the man's hand. He would trot forward a few steps, by way of encouraging his master to continue the climb.

Never at such times would he leave Scott and scamper on ahead with the other dogs, nor follow the human members of the climbing party.

Even when he knew a picnic lunch had been spread at the hilltop, just beyond, he stayed with his tired master, rather than to revel in the food scraps which were awaiting him at the feast.

His one drawback as a companion on walks was his fixed belief that it was his duty to thrash any other dog he and Scott chanced to meet in the course of these rambles. The larger the dog, the better Camp liked the scrimmage.

As a result, there was an endless succession of dogfights to enliven all Scott's walks. And there were endless complaints from neighbors, high and low, because of Camp's quenchless battle lust.

The dogs of the region either feared him or else they established death feuds with him.

Camp reveled in his unpopularity and in his state of chronic warfare. Scott did not. Nothing but his love for the pugnacious little crossbreed could have made the novelist put up with such a continuous state of turmoil.

But Scott's annoyance at his chum's belligerence was

far outweighed by his admiration for the dog's accomplishments and his amusing qualities. He wrote of Camp as the wisest dog he had known. He continued the eulogy thus:

"I taught him to understand a great many words, insomuch that I am positive the communication between ourselves and the canine species might be greatly enlarged.

"Camp bit the baker who was bringing bread to our family. I beat him and explained the enormity of his offense. After which, to the last minute of his life, he never heard the least allusion to the story (in whatever voice or tone) without getting up and retiring to the darkest corner of the room with every appearance of distress.

"Then if you would say: 'The baker was well paid' or 'The baker was not hurt at all,' Camp came forth from his hiding place, and capered and barked and rejoiced."

The dog had a perilous illness. Scott laid aside his own work and nursed him back to health. When Camp was twelve he died. A strenuous lifetime of battles with other dogs and of guarding his master's welfare had taken heavy toll of his strength.

Scott buried him in his garden, digging the grave himself. He was heartsick at the loss of the loyal little halfbreed. The next evening he himself was to be guest of honor at a public dinner in Edinburgh. He wrote to the chairman of the dinner, saying he would be unable to attend it, "because of the death of a dear old friend."

There were a half score dogs, at various times, later,

in the Scott household. But over and above them all arises the memory of Maida, the huge staghound that was monarch of all Abbotsford's animal population—save only the cat. A letter from Scott, written in 1816, tells of the arrival of Maida at his home:

"I have got from my friend Glengarry the noblest dog seen on the Border since Johnny Armstrong's day. He is between the wolf and the deerhound, about six feet from tip of nose to tip of tail; high and strong in proportion . . . gentle and a great favorite. He will eat without being to the trouble to put a paw on chair or table."

I have spoken of the family cat which alone did not acknowledge Maida's supremacy. Scott wrote:

"He (the cat) keeps him in the greatest possible order, and insists on all 'rights of precedence'; and scratches with impunity the nose of an animal who would make no bones of a wolf and who pulls down a red deer without fear or difficulty.

"I heard Maida set up some most piteous howls. And I assure you the noise was no joke. It was all occasioned by his fear of passing Puss who had stationed himself on the stairs."

Washington Irving, visiting Abbotsford, met and admired Maida. So did many another celebrity from both sides of the Atlantic who paid pilgrimages to Scott's loved home. Landseer painted the great hound—Maida hated to pose for his portrait—and Blore did the same. Only Blore outdid Landseer; by bribing the hound, with luscious bones, to sit still and be painted.

Full of years, Maida died. Scott followed Byron's

example by building for him a monument above the grave in the garden at Abbotsford—a monument surmounted by Maida's stone statue—and by decreeing the carving of a two-line Latin verse above Maida's head. Badly translated into modern English the Latin couplet may be read:

> *Under this effigy,—your form, of late,—*
> *Maida, sleep soundly at your Master's gate!*

Then there were Charles Dickens' dogs—a noble and an ignoble army of them, first and last—led by the author's best-loved and worst-behaved "Spanish mastiff," Sultan. It is of Sultan I am going to ask your leave to tell you. He was, to me, more worth talking about than all the rest of Dickens' many dogs put together.

In letters, the novelist described Sultan as an enormous young animal, buff of coat and jet-black of muzzle. And he told many odd things about Sultan and about his career. We must take those statements more or less as established facts. For Dickens' own books prove his close knowledge of dogs—from Dora's diminutive terrier, Jip, in *David Copperfield*, to Bill Sikes's formidable mongrel bulldog in *Oliver Twist*.

Yes, Dickens was a dogman, by choice and by long experience. So let us accept a large Spanish mastiff, with buff coat and black muzzle, as a recognized (if temporary) breed, and get on with Sultan's life story:

As a half-starved and ragged little boy, Dickens had been wont to stop on the road to Rochester and stare through the iron pickets at a rural estate named "Gadshill." With a child's terrible earnestness he swore that someday he would own Gadshill and would live there.

It was well after his acquisition of his Gadshill estate that Dickens acquired Sultan, the "Spanish mastiff."

I have no record among my massed sheets of notes, nor in my dog library, as to how the novelist acquired Sultan. My recollection is that the dog was given to him, in puppyhood, by a London friend. But, from the outset, Dickens and Sultan were dear chums.

Their companionship was a joy to the dog. It seems to have been fraught with tons of annoyance and of embarrassment for the "mastiff's" owner. Also to Dickens' oversize family and to his neighbors.

Sultan's first dramatic deed after his arrival at Gadshill, as a puppy, was to swallow at a single gulp his new master's favorite kitten. After that, he ravened jocosely and fatally among the rest of Gadshill's smaller livestock.

Every living thing, little enough, was fodder for his ravenous maw and for his zest for catching and killing. His nightly rambles through the neighborhood were followed by floods of protesting letters from folk whose smug grounds he had invaded.

Homeward the dog would trot at dawn, bloodsmeared and tired, yet with his stout steel muzzle still in place around his jaws. Dickens wrote to a London acquaintance (perhaps the man who had given the mastiff to him):

"Sultan has grown amazingly. He is a sight. But he is so accursedly fierce to other dogs that I am obliged to take him out, muzzled. He has taken an invincible repugnance to soldiers; which in a military district like this is inconvenient.

"Such is his spirit that, with his muzzle tight on, yesterday, he dashed into a company of infantry marching past our house, and pulled down one private. Except under such provocation, he is as gentle and as docile with me as a dog can possibly be."

In spite of his eccentricities, Sultan was devoted to Dickens. Many a long and happy hike did they have together through the sweet English summer countryside. The mastiff might be—and was—murderously or mischievously fierce with strangers and a terror to other quadrupeds. Yet with his master he was as gentle as the traditional lamb.

As fast as Sultan outrode one unlucky escapade, another came to take its place and to turn peaceful Gadshill into turmoil and crass excitement. Here is a newer episode in Sultan's life, as set forth in a Dickens letter (a letter published afterward in a British newspaper):

"Last night the gardener fired at some man in the garden upon whom he came suddenly and who kicked him in a dangerous manner. I immediately turned out, unloosed Sultan and hunted the vagabond.

"We could not get hold of him. But the intelligence of the dog and his delighted confidence he imparted to me as we stumbled across country in the dark, were quite enchanting.

"Two policemen, appearing in the distance and making a professional show of energy, had a narrow escape.

"As Sultan was in the act of rushing at them, I

was obliged to hold him around the neck with both arms and to call upon the police force to vanish in an inglorious manner."

In spite of the huge dog's eccentricities, Dickens loved him more and more. And the love was reciprocated a thousandfold. In another letter (presumably to the dog's giver) he said:

"I cannot thank you too much for Sultan. He is a noble fellow. He has fallen into the ways of our family with the grace and dignity which denote a gentleman. He comes down to the railway to welcome me home with a profound absence of interest in my individual opinion of him which captivates me completely.

"I am going to take him around the country with me and improve his acquaintance. You will find a complete understanding between us, I hope, when you next come here."

This sounds promising and optimistic enough. And apparently Dickens gave the experiment a fair trial. But its results were not what had been hoped. As witness his next letter to the same man:

"He" (Sultan) "went off today to have a sort of prizefight with a dog of his own size and weight and age, residing at some distance from here. After a terrible battle, Sultan left his adversary almost for dead."

That meant cash payment to be handed out by the ever-thrifty author, to whom the needless spending of a sixpence was always a grief. And in the months that followed there was much more money to be shelled out by him for real or claimed damages inflicted by his mastiff in various parts of the surrounding countryside.

One verified complaint after another, against the

predatory Sultan, poured in to Gadshill. One sorely grudged goldpiece after another did Dickens part with to satisfy these angry complaints.

Money had been pouring in upon Dickens in an aureate stream for years, from his writings. He was the best-paid author in Great Britain. Best-paid author and best-paid lecturer in America too. But in his youth he had known black poverty. It had taught him grim facts as to the value of money. And he began to grudge tossing gold into a throng of outstretched hands in payment for Sultan's misdeeds.

Then came the long-accumulating climax:

The little daughter of a neighbor was on her way back from school. As she came to the home of the renowned author whose books she loved so well, she halted at the open gateway of Gadshill. She stared into the grounds, in the hope of a glimpse of the renowned Charles Dickens.

Sultan, from the front steps, saw her loitering there. He rushed to the attack.

The child made the mistake of crying out and kicking at him, since she had no time to try to run away.

(This is a fatal error when even a tolerably good-natured dog comes running toward you. Don't run. Don't cry out. Don't kick or strike. Stand calmly and unmoving, with your hands on your chest and your feet together. Do this, and do it without show of fright, and talk meanwhile to your assailant in a steady and quiet voice. And not once in twenty times will the most vicious dog bite you. That irrelevant tip is worth your remembering. One day you may need it.)

The child screeched in terror. Hysterically she kicked

at the onrushing Sultan. And the result was what might have been expected.

The dog's fangs dug deep into the calf of the kicking leg. The shrieking child was thrown to the ground. Gardeners and house servants came up on the run and dragged Sultan from his prey. The victim was hustled to a doctor for treatment. The mastiff was chained securely.

But the mischief was done.

The neighbors were roused to a pitch of red-hot indignation. The law intervened. The parents of the injured child prepared to bring suit for heavy damages against Sultan's illustrious owner. Public feeling everywhere ran high.

Dickens seemed to be in for more trouble than he could carry with any degree of comfort. Also for a bigger money expenditure than he liked to think of. His cash pocket was due to be punctured even more deeply and painfully than the child's leg had been.

He paid the goodly sum demanded for the settling of the case. There was nothing else for him to do. Then he condemned Sultan to death.

He ordered his head gardener to take the dog out to a distant part of the estate early next morning and shoot him.

Dickens' daughter wrote thus of what followed:

"Yesterday morning the gardener took Sultan to the end of the meadow and shot him. And he was buried in a field. The poor dog dropped without a struggle or even a cry. I am happy to say the execution was performed as skillfully and as mercifully as it could be done.

"But I can't tell you how terrible it was! We all heard the shot. We went to bed the night before dreading it. And I don't think any of us slept an hour."

Dickens wrote a letter that described the needful killing; and he followed it with this eulogy of his slain mastiff:

"He was the finest dog I ever saw. Between me and him there was a perfect understanding. But, to adopt the popular phrase, the understanding between us was so very confidential that it 'went no further.' His execution was very affecting."

So much for the fate of a magnificent dog, but a dog that had no more place in a peaceful English country home than has a mailed Visigoth at a village prayer meeting.

There must be thousands of Wellesley College alumnae, and many more residents of the town of Wellesley, who have vivid memories of Sigurd, the collie made famous by the writings of his mistress, Katharine Lee Bates. As I have told you, Miss Bates was my loved friend. It was my high privilege to write the foreword for the revised edition of her book, *Sigurd, Our Golden Collie*.

The dog had free run of Wellesley's campus and lecture halls and of the whole neighborhood. His friends were legion. But his one devotion was centered on his owner. At least, as far as devotion and loyalty did not interfere with his "own-your-own-soul" ideas of life and his love for mischief and for wandering far from home.

These wanderings did not always coincide with the

paths of duty and of his mistress' plans. As when Sigurd was cast for an important role in a college play. It was a patriotic drama. He was to enact the trusty dog of a Revolutionary soldier who had been thrown into prison. Sigurd was to rescue the hero from his cell.

The part was built around a favorite trick of Sigurd's: his lifelong habit of leaping on anyone who burst suddenly into a room.

In the play, the hero and his loyal collie were to be discovered sitting gloomily in the former's cell, on the eve of his hanging. A turnkey was to burst excitedly into the room. Sigurd was to leap at the intruder's chest.

Under the violent impact, the turnkey was to fall backward, stunned, to the floor. Over his body the hero was to run through the open doorway of the cell, followed by the dog, and to make his escape.

The entire plot of the drama hung on this escape. Thus it hung on Sigurd's perfect work in the cell scene.

Many were the rehearsals. Always, the collie's acting was everything that could be asked for. He reveled in it all. He gave a thrilling enactment of a dog leaping in fury on his master's turnkey-enemy and bearing him to the ground. Then he bounded offstage, in the wake of the hero, with a gay zest inspired by a piece of raw meat held out to him temptingly by Miss Bates who was stationed in the wings.

It was eminently satisfactory, this bit of canine rescue work. Miss Bates and everyone concerned were confident it would go through flawlessly on the night of the actual performance.

Which proves how little they knew of the eccentricities of canine nature. As they could have learned from anyone who has tried to steer the best-rehearsed dogs through a series of action photographs or motion-picture scenes. The average clever dog will put on a finely snappy and realistic act—at home or in rehearsal. But when it comes to the performance itself—well, that is on the knees of the gods. As the Wellesley players were to find out.

Early on the morning of the day set for the play's première, Miss Bates had several volunteer aides give Sigurd a thorough bath, scrubbing him industriously, then using up a tubful of crash towels to rub him dry They brushed and combed and scoured his heavy coat until it fluffed out like a halo of burnished gold edged with snow.

Sigurd was miserable, but magnificent, from all this multiple grooming. He was the more disgusted when, after a carefully supervised walk, he was shut indoors. His mistress did not intend that the toil of beautifying him for the evening's audience to admire should be wasted. He was in the pink of perfection. And in the pink of perfection he must stay till the performance.

Sigurd did nothing of the kind.

To soothe his own bath-outraged feelings he nosed a back door open and ran away to the woods and thence to the swamp and the briar patches beyond. He had a disreputably happy day, chasing squirrels, splashing through swamp mud, snarling his new-washed coat with a million cockleburs.

Meantime, at Wellesley, consternation ran riot. The hour for the curtain's rise was perilously near. And the canine star could not be found: the four-footed actor on whose rescue work the course of the play depended. Scouts were sent forth in vain to search for the wanderer. There was no trace of him anywhere.

As Miss Bates sat despairingly at home, just before the moment set for the rise of the curtain, Sigurd breezed into the house.

There was a sigh of relief from his owner and from her worried guests at the dog's return. By rushing him to the theater he might yet be in time—if barely in time—for his Big Scene.

But the instant of relief was followed by a gasp of crass horror as Sigurd advanced farther into the lamplight.

He was smeared all over with mud and crusted with burs. His once-glorious coat was lank with swamp water. It clung to him in grotesque hideousness. His appearance on the stage, in that condition, would evoke Homeric howls of mirth from even the friendliest of college audiences.

Moreover, it was indescribably evident that one of his many woodland adventures during the day had involved an encounter with a skunk.

It was a moment for despair. But Miss Bates refused to give up hope. She ceased, for the instant, to be a college dean and the author of *America the Beautiful* and of other ringing poems. She became, instead, the commanding general of a stricken field.

She sent word to the theater that Sigurd had come home, and that the curtain was to be held till his arrival back-stage. Then she and her guests fell to work with feverish haste on the foully bedraggled collie, to make him as nearly presentable as possible.

There was no chance of duplicating his gorgeous appearance of twelve hours earlier. But the worst of the mud could be scrubbed from his sopping wet coat and the worst of the burs combed from it. With luck and skill, he could be made no worse looking—though far worse smelling—than the average scarecrow. And he could go through his part in the play.

This time Sigurd offered little of the bath resistance which had been his in the morning. He was worn out and comfortably sleepy after his day of forest running. His chief ambition, just then, was to take a long and refreshing nap, rather than to squirm insurgently in the grasp of his bathers and brushers. So the task of making him less abhorrent to the eye—even if not to the nose—was comparatively easy.

When the ablutions were finished, Sigurd was bundled into a carriage and taken to the theater. There, the audience already had begun to clap, in impatience at the delay in raising the curtain.

Miss Bates held her collie securely by the ruff during the earlier action of the play, lest again he decamp. Then came his Big Scene. She led him onto the stage, set now as a prison cell, and deposited him at the side of the luckless young hero who sat despondently on a prison cot—a cot borrowed from one of the college dormitories.

Up went the curtain.

There was a round of applause at sight of all-popular Sigurd standing there beside the captive soldier. For some reason the collie looked damper and more bedraggled and less shiningly clean and alert than they were wont to see him. But that was a negligible detail.

Then across the footlights and through the auditorium was wafted a strange and horrid stench that permeated the whole house. Skunk aroma is not dissipated by a single sketchy bath when once it has imbedded itself in the mattress-thick coat of a collie.

The condemned hero patted his devoted dog on the head, trying not to let the ghastly odor choke him. Then he strode forward to speak his brief soliloquy before the turnkey should burst into the cell. He whistled softly to Sigurd to accompany him, as usual, downstage.

But Sigurd had far different ideas. Forgotten was the long and patient rehearsing to which he had responded so brilliantly. Forgotten was everything except that he was dead tired, and that he craved sleep above all other things in life.

Behind him was the soft dormitory cot, such a couch as he had taken many a cozy nap on. Sigurd climbed wearily up onto its counterpane and curled himself for the doze he needed so badly. Immediately he was miles deep in the slumber of utter exhaustion.

As far as he was concerned the evening's activities were very definitely at an end. He was through. Providence had endowed him, miraculously, with a soft bed to sleep on. Nothing else mattered in the very least. He slept. And as he slept he snored.

The hero's doleful soliloquy ended. The turnkey, at his cue, threw open the door of the cell to lead him to execution. Sigurd snored on, with increasing loudness.

There was a dreadful stage wait. The hero blinked

worriedly at the dead-asleep collie which should have flung himself upon the turnkey. The turnkey blinked at the dog, too, and wondered what to do next.

Then the hero did some quick improvising that was worthy of a much more experienced actor. He (or she) declaimed:

"Ah! You have even drugged my faithful hound that might have saved me. Scoundrel!"

Rushing at the turnkey he dealt him a light slap somewhere in the region of the chest. The turnkey took the hint and fell to the floor, unconscious. The hero sprang over his fallen body, as per schedule, and escaped through the doorway.

Sigurd snored on, peacefully, as the curtain came down; and for several hours thereafter.

The audience were generous in their applause. This, while the ushers tiptoed around, shutting windows in an attempt to bar out the skunk reek which seemed to be wafted into the building from somewhere in the outer darkness of the night.

Sigurd's first and last stage experience is still an oft-told tale at Wellesley.

The next spring, the college was stirred by the news that a renowned Englishwoman—a poet and a mystic—was to address the students in a right exalted lecture. I am going to quote from Miss Bates's own account of the experience:

"An English lady—a presence like a flame—was one afternoon addressing a choice assemblage in our oriental parlor on the 'Mysteries of the Bahaist Faith.' A torchbearer of the Persian prophet, she was telling of her first interview with Ali Baha on Mount Carmel:

" 'And the Master greeted me thus: Oh, Child of the Kingdom——!'

"*Bump* went something against the door, which swung wide, admitting Sigurd, who saluted the company with a comprehensive wag of his tail.

" 'You beautiful creature!' cried the Englishwoman, winning him to her with an outstretched hand. 'I am sure *you* are a Child of the Kingdom!'

"And Sigurd wagged, came up for a pat, and then dropped down at her feet to slumber out the rest of her impassioned discourse, waking promptly with the arrival of refreshments."

I don't know the name of the English lecturer—and never before or since have I heard of the theme of her lecture. But I say: All honor to her!

When he was nearly eleven, Sigurd was hit by a crazily driven motorcar, as so many thousands of friendly and harmless dogs have been smitten by such modern Juggernaut vehicles—vehicles driven by folk who never would have been deemed worthy of a pistol permit and yet who are allowed freely to handle a machine fiftyfold more murderous than any firearm yet invented.

Sigurd was not killed. But he was badly hurt. Never wholly did he recover from the injury and shock of the blow.

In 1919, my own golden collie "Treve," hero of my book of that name, was born. So much like Miss Bates's immortal dog was he in looks and in elfin originality that I asked—and received—her gracious permission to register him with the American Kennel Club as "Sunnybank Sigurd."

But the shouted summons: "Sigurd!" bore a too-close resemblance to "Sic 'im!" It caused sudden and vociferous strife when it was voiced in the presence of a bunch of rollicking collies.

So, on the eve of a long absence from Sunnybank, I told my English superintendent, Robert Friend, to think up a "kennel name" for the youngster: one whose utterance should lead to fewer fights.

On my return home, months later, I found he had taught the pup to answer to the call of "Treve." I asked Robert Friend where and how he had evolved such a name. In entire good faith he made reply:

"You teach your dogs to retrieve, don't you, boss? Well, hasn't a dog got to learn to treve before he can learn to *re*trieve?"

The explanation was so sublimely asinine that it hit my fancy. And Champion Sunnybank Sigurd was known as "Treve" for the rest of his meteoric short life.

There are innumerable dogs of all breeds and of no describable breeds, through the country today, which answer to that name. All are called so in memory of my golden collie. For, assuredly, never before was the appellation, "Treve," tacked to any dog. Robert Friend's deduction as to treving and *re*trieving has added a wholly new name to the canine directory.

Going back to the dogs of real authors:

There was Diamond; of course, Diamond the spaniel which caused his master, Sir Isaac Newton, to go to smash for months with a nervous and mental breakdown. For a couple of centuries and more the story of Diamond has been told as a sample of his master's perfect temper control.

I am going to tell it once again, but in few words. Even this shoddiest anthology of authors' dogs won't be complete without the ancient, if now-doubted, yarn.

Newton had been engaged for years in compiling notes and statistics from all sources for his monumental monograph on Optics. At last the vast pile of material was ready for whipping into shape.

He left the thick sheaves of notes and references stacked neatly on his wide study table, late one winter afternoon, when he went to vesper services at a church near his rooms. His little spaniel, Diamond, went nearly everywhere at the scientist's heels. So the dog now prepared friskingly to follow Newton from the room.

But spaniels were not allowed to attend church—though often in the Scottish Highlands you may see collies lying decorously at their shepherd masters' feet during long sermons—so Newton ordered the dog back into the study, and shut the door behind him.

Perhaps the immortal scientist was too much engrossed in persuading Diamond to give up the idea of a walk and to stay patiently at home to notice he had left three candles burning on the table: candles he had lighted a few minutes earlier, as the winter dusk closed in.

It is not wise to leave oil lamps or candles burning in a room whose only occupant is a frisky dog. Much loss has been incurred and much insurance money has been paid because of just such carelessness.

Newton came back from vespers in due time. The

stairway leading to his study was clouded with smoke. As the study door was flung wide, a blinding gush of it billowed forth into the entry. From end to end, the big table was ablaze.

One of the three candlesticks lay on its side amid piles of flaming paper. Diamond cowered, yelping with fear, at the farthest end of the room.

Seeking amusement or exercise, in his master's absence, the spaniel had jumped onto the table's broad surface. The jump had upset a candlestick. The candle's flame had ignited the nearest sheaf of notes. The dry paper—on a dryer topic—had blazed up. From it the rest of the table's heaps of documents had caught fire.

Diamond had fled to a corner, squealing in terror. By the time Newton came back from church, the literary labor of years had been destroyed.

Other members of the household caught the reek of smoke and came running into the room. They put out the blaze before it could travel beyond the table and to the rug beneath it.

Newton was of no help to them in this emergency labor. Dazed, moveless, he stood staring from the smouldering material for his book to the whining spaniel in the corner. Then, according to the volunteer fire fighters who crowded the room, he said gently:

"Oh, Diamond, you little know the mischief you've done!"

That was all. He did not punish the brute. He did not fly into a very justifiable rage. He was in a trance. The despair of his frightful loss had robbed him of all power to think or to feel. He was benumbed.

And benumbed he was for months thereafter. His mind refused to work in normal fashion. His nerves were dead. Doctors wrought over him, in vain; until such time as nature began to absorb the shock. Then very slowly he regained his power to think and to work.

If he had failed to get well, the world might have waited another century or more—because of a wretched little spaniel!—for Newton's Theory of the Attraction of Gravitation.

Alexander Pope—inspired poet and satirist and essayist—was twisted and deformed and was almost repulsive to look on. (The third lame dog owner in this chapter!) And his disposition was as crabbed as his body. His tongue and his trenchant pen dripped vitriol. Thus, he had enemies everywhere and in all walks of life.

His infirmities made it hard for him to defend himself against anyone who might choose to wreak a dislike by beating him up or by more serious punishment. But this feebleness was compensated by the constant presence of his giant great Dane, Bounce.

Bounce seemed to realize his master's need for protection. For he appointed himself Pope's day-and-night guard. Everywhere the swarthy and crooked little poet was followed by the majestic big dog. Bounce was gentleness itself to Pope. But toward much of the rest of the world he was surlily unresponsive and sometimes ferocious. For example:

Pope hired a new valet. The man appeared to be an

excellent servant. The poet was much pleased with him. The dog was not.

There was no excuse, it seemed, for Bounce's instant and implacable hatred for the man. The valet tried to make friends with him. But the Dane flew at

ALEXANDER POPE'S BOUNCE

him in sizzling fury. Pope intervened, scolding and striking his dog, and bidding him leave the new servant alone.

Outwardly—and whenever Pope could catch him in time—Bounce obeyed. But it was evident he carried the feud as fiercely as ever.

In the daytime, Bounce was with his master. So a sharp word from Pope could, and did, curb any attempt at mayhem on the valet. But at night it was different.

It was the servant's duty to prepare Pope for bed, to draw the curtains, etc., and to come in again early in the morning to open the blinds and to bring his employer's cup of chocolate and to fill his bath.

As Pope was likely to be asleep when the man came into the bedroom in the morning, and as Bounce always was vigilantly awake at the foot of the bed at such times, there was danger of the dog attacking before his master could wake and call him off.

The only way to avert this was to leave the dog out-of-doors all night. That was done.

On the first night afterward, Pope was awakened by a slight sound in his room. Peeping through the curtains he saw in the faint moonlight a crouching figure, knife in hand, moving stealthily toward the bed.

Pope was unarmed and he was a cripple. He knew he could have no chance against the intruder. And on this night, of all nights, he had shut the formidable Bounce outdoors. But his valet slept in an anteroom, and might possibly wake in time to save his employer.

Pope shouted for help at the top of his puny lungs. The knifer leaped forward. So did something else.

The long french window of the ground-floor bedroom was smashed in, as if by a battering-ram. Amid a rainstorm of broken glass, Bounce cleared half the width of the room at one leap; and was ravening at the marauder's throat.

Down went the man on his back, borne to the floor by that flying weight. In vain he strove to stab the murderous beast and to wriggle free and escape through the broken window. None of these things could he do.

Meantime, Pope was adding his own cries to the unearthly duet of canine roars and human screams, and he was tugging like mad at the bell ropes.

Into the room barged his servants and his housekeeper, sketchily attired, carrying lights. Gardeners ran up from their sleeping quarters in the grounds.

Bounce was pried free of his half-dead victim. The man was tied, hand and foot, while the constables were sent for.

Then, and only then, the prisoner's bloodsmeared and fear-twisted features were recognized as those of the efficient new valet.

According to one account current at the time, the fellow had gained a position with Pope in order to rob him, and the knife was carried only as a means of terrorizing the cripple in case the alarm were given. Another version of the crime's motive is that the pseudo-valet was hired by Pope's political enemies and satire victims to assassinate him.

In either case, the attempt was a spectacular failure. All because a big dog had taken a first-sight hatred to the stranger, and because that dog's queer instinct had made him lie on guard just outside the window of the ground-floor bedroom from which he had been barred.

Bounce may have had an occult inkling, from the start, as to the valet's character and intentions. But I doubt it. More likely it was one of those seemingly causeless prejudices that occur so often in one-man dogs. The dislike may have been strengthened by jealousy of the man who was performing such continuous personal services for Bounce's deity.

In any event, it was a hatred which saved Pope's life. Thenceforth the crooked man was as wholesouledly devoted to Bounce as always Bounce had been devoted to him.

When Pope went to Bath for a short visit, he was forced to leave the great Dane at his Twickenham home on the hill above the Thames. To Lady Mary Wortley Montagu he wrote of departing from home and of "having kissed Bounce, who is my one friend there." (I am sorry Pope was a dog-kisser. In my own perhaps worthless opinion, dogs are far too normal and chumlike to be slobbered over. I don't believe they like any kissing. I would as soon think of kissing a goat or a wart hog.)

So renowned did Bounce become, through his master's writings and through a poem of John Gay's and from other sources, that the Prince of Wales asked for one of his puppies. Pope sent the youngster to Kew, where the royal family were in residence. On the pup's collar he caused this couplet to be engraved:

I am His Highness' dog, at Kew,
Pray tell me, sir, whose dog are you?

The elder Alexandre Dumas was escorted around his estate and through the Paris streets by a small mob of his dogs, most of them nondescript mongrels. For the old quadroon genius had a way with animals. Stray curs were forever following him home and electing to stay there with him. He had not the heart or the inclination to drive them away.

His steward complained bitterly to him:

"The whole house is overrun with these miserable brutes. There are no fewer than thirteen of them now."

"Thirteen?" echoed Dumas in horror. "I had no idea of that. We must correct it immediately. Go out and find me another dog. Thirteen is an unlucky number."

I suppose no cursory account of great authors' dogs would be complete without saying something about Elizabeth Barrett Browning's spaniel, Flush; renowned in song and letters and in drama.

Here, my short mention of Flush will be made with no enthusiasm at all. I never was able to work up any personal interest in his smug career, except for the fact that London dog thieves drew rich dividends for a long time by stealing him and holding him for reward—a reward his poet-mistress paid eagerly.

When Elizabeth Barrett eloped with Robert Browning, from Wimpole Street and from the jealous wrath of her crotchety old father who heatedly ordered the spaniel's death, Flush was lugged along, squirming and snarling, under his invalid mistress' arm, to the carriage which was to carry the elopers to the train, which in turn was to carry them to the Channel boat. The tossing boat which was to bear them on the first transpontine stage toward their ultimate home—at the old gray house of my boyhood memories, on the far bank of the river Arno, in a grim and ancient riverside street.

The house still is named "Casa Guidi" and the wall bears a carven emblem on it to the general effect that Mrs Browning bound Italy to England in a hoop of gold.

There the spectacular and (to me) uninteresting Flush lived on to old age, and at last was buried in the Casa Guidi's cellar.

Peace to Flush's over-advertised memory!

CHAPTER VII
Ghost Dogs

I DON'T WANT TO WRITE this chapter of your book and mine. At the outset let me say I am not on record as believing or as disbelieving any of its anecdotes.

I am going to tell you certain authenticated tales. And I am going to give my authority for all of them, as well as my own (perhaps wrong) opinions as to the truth of some.

Believe them or not. I am not vouching for the veracity of any of them. Even though a few are backed by evidence strong enough to hang an archbishop or to stand a Supreme Court veracity test. Here goes, and read or not, as you see fit.

I am going to begin with the solemnly attested experience of the Rev. Isaac Woodcock, of Beverley Parish in Yorkshire, England—an experience of his which dated from 1854.

It has been printed and reprinted. It has been published of recent years in steadfast good faith, in the *Methodist Recorder,* one of Great Britain's strongest and most venerated religious publications.

I tell it here, without adding any details of my own imagining, only reminding you that the tale has been current in northern England for the best part of a century, and that the *Methodist Recorder* is the accepted organ of a mighty religious denomination and is not a fly-by-night sensational newsprint.

Let me say I do not doubt the Rev. Isaac Woodcock's statements in any details—nor those of any other well-confirmed "supernatural" anecdotes I shall cite here. But I *do* doubt and discount the deductions Woodcock and other narrators draw from their experiences. In fact, I don't believe one detail of most of those deductions.

I may be wrong in imputing wholly normal and natural and non-occult solutions to the unquestioned facts I shall set forth. But I am too materialistic to believe these incidents cannot be explained on normal grounds.

I may be mistaken, but I refuse to believe in spooks until I am convinced that their alleged performances cannot be accounted for by logical and mundane explanations.

Now, if you like, we'll start on the Rev. Isaac Woodcock's skin-prickling adventures. They are worth your reading. And remember what I have just told you of the secular and sacred testimony to their veracity.

Let's go:

Woodcock was at the head of several widely scattered parishes. He went from one to the other of them alone and unarmed, though there were plenty of tough characters sprinkled through the region and though sometimes he carried fairly large sums of charity money.

He had no fear. When his wife or his friends remonstrated with him for this rashness, he met all their arguments with the same reply: that he was safe from danger. To prove this he would quote to them the Biblical text:

"The Angel of the Lord encampeth round about them that fear Him, and delivereth them."

Collections for missions had been raised in the various parishes. The moneys from these, together with certain clerical reports, were to be turned over to Mr Woodcock at a meeting to be held at a rural chapel a few miles from Beverley, one evening in the early winter of 1854.

Mr Woodcock had been in the saddle all day on one of his tours of inspection. He would not compel his tired horse to carry him to and from the meeting, but decided to go on foot. Most of the route lay through patches of woodland and between the hedgerow boundaries of fields.

When the meeting was ended, late in the evening, the clergyman started back alone toward Beverley. In his pockets was the collection money. He planned to take it next day to the local bank. Meanwhile, he made himself gladly responsible for its safety.

Although the holding of the meeting and its purpose were well known to the neighborhood, Mr Woodcock felt no anxiety for his own safety nor for that of the rather large sum of collection money he was carrying. As always, he relied implicitly on the strength of the sacred promise in the text he quoted so often.

As he strode through a strip of woods, he heard the fast padding of feet close behind. In the dim light, he could see an immense shaggy dog trotting up to him. The dog licked the man's hand, then fell gravely into step at his side.

Presently, as they neared the end of the woods, the animal showed strong signs of worry. From one side of Mr Woodcock to the other he shifted, peering ahead. Then he began to growl savagely.

The menace was not directed toward his human companion. So the minister paid no special heed to it; supposing the dog had scented or sighted a cat or some woodland creature that was straying in quest of food.

Just ahead, the lane wound between two thick hedgerows. Here it was less dark than under the trees. And here the dog sprang forward, roaring in angry threat. Outlined against the skyline, the minister could see three men's heads just above the hedgerow to the left.

It was at these men the dog had dashed, with that deafening roar. They ducked out of sight. The dog did not follow them, but dropped back to his chosen place at Mr Woodcock's side.

There he paced for several minutes. Then, wheeling, he snarled savagely and started back along the lane. Again the minister could see the heads of the three men. They had been trailing him ever since the dog had voiced his roaring challenge.

It was evident that their very natural fear of a brute so formidable and savage had outweighed their desire to rob the man the dog was guarding. Yet they had followed, stealthily, on a chance of eluding the brute and of getting hold of the money.

The dog resumed his place beside the clergyman, darting keenly suspicious glances backward or from side to side. But the men had had enough. They did not come again within sight of the two travelers.

Soon, just in front, appeared the town of Beverley, with its friendly lights and its friendlier folk and its police. The dog licked Mr Woodcock's hand once more, whimpering softly.

Then—so the clergyman declared a hundred times later and with awed solemnity—the creature *vanished*. Seemingly into thin air.

Mr Woodcock whistled and called, but in vain. Next morning he made a round of the vicinity, for miles in all directions. Nobody had seen the huge beast. Nobody had heard of such a dog owned by any neighbor.

To the end of his days, Mr Woodcock believed it was a supernatural apparition sent from heaven to protect him on that night of peril.

The records show that he was a man of honor and of pure godliness, and that his word was not to be doubted. He would conclude his verbal or written narrative of the strange occurrence by quoting triumphantly his loved text concerning "the Angel of the Lord" guarding and delivering "them that fear Him."

Now, I don't doubt for an instant that the clergyman was telling the truth—as to the dog's escorting him home and scaring footpads away. Nor do I doubt he believed wholeheartedly that the beast was a supernatural visitor and that it vanished before his eyes.

But isn't it far more likely that a wandering flesh-and-blood dog, perhaps straying many miles from home and lonely for human companionship, had seen Mr Woodcock walking through the woods that night, and had taken a liking to him and decided to share his journey?

Almost all of us can recall a strange dog's joining us in a stroll, at some time or other, and making friends with us. It is an everyday happening, and it is wholly in keeping with canine nature.

Having adopted Mr Woodcock, temporarily, as a chum, it is quite natural the dog should have turned on the thieves who sought to rob him.

More than once, in my old hiking days, a dog has trotted up to me and elected himself my fellow hiker. More than once, too, such a dog has growled at acquaintances of mine who, he thought, came over-near to me on the road. Most dogmen have had a like experience.

And none of us has attributed it to anything more occult than a lonesome canine's wish to go for a stroll with some likable human. We sensed nothing supernatural in a normal animal's normal behavior.

Dogs like to go for a walk. Dogs take sudden likings to occasional strangers. Watchdog instinct prompts some of them to attack folk who seem to menace those strangers.

"It needs no ghost, my lord, come from the grave, to tell us this."

So much, I think, to account for Mr Woodcock's experience. For all of it, at least, except the miraculous vanishing of his guardian dog. And, to me, that is the simplest part of it.

If you take a long walk, by night, in forest or fields, and then come suddenly upon the bright lights of streets and of houses, several seconds will elapse before your eyes can adjust themselves with any accuracy to the glare.

At the edge of Beverley, the guardian dog seemed to Mr Woodcock to disappear in miraculous fashion.

Isn't it far more likely that the beast trotted back noiselessly into the darkness or else slipped into the nearest doorway for a nap? This before the clergyman's dazzled eyes could focus squarely upon him? A dog's motions are not always easy—or possible—to trace distinctly at night.

I can't see anything remarkable in Mr Woodcock's failure to find news of the supposed ghost when he made inquiries throughout the vicinity next day. Remember, this was in a section of Yorkshire where sheep raising was one of the chief forms of livelihood. Remember, too, that dogs were ever under suspicion as sheep killers.

When strangers rode from house to house, describing some dog and asking questions, the inference was that it was wanted for sheep killing. The owner of such a dog—or any well-wisher of his owner—would be likely to deny having seen or heard of the animal.

So much, I verily believe, for the probable solution of the Guardian Dog mystery!

Mr Woodcock's experience was not unique, even in those days. Nearly a quarter century earlier, another missionary-cleric had similar protection lavished on him by a similar shaggy dog. (See *The Life of Blessèd Don Bosco,* by Alfred C. Auffray.)

Once the creature dispersed a group of thieves which waylaid Don Bosco on the way to the bank. Again, he scattered a group of hoodlums who were assailing the missionary's home. Again he thrust Don Bosco back indoors when two men lay in wait across the road to shoot him as he came out.

As soon as the town became safe and the police had driven the rougher element away and jailed most of its ringleaders, the dog vanished, as did Mr Woodcock's protector. Nor could any news of him be gleaned from wholesale inquiries.

But Don Bosco went Mr Woodcock one better:

Twenty-seven years after the vanishing, the missionary was on a journey to a town where he was to preach. He was on foot. A heavy rain was sluicing down. He lost his way. He wandered aimlessly, drenched and chilled to the bone.

It was then, according to his sworn statement, that the same mystic dog loomed up before him and guided him to the light and safety of the town that was his destination. Then, as with Mr Woodcock, the creature melted into nothingness.

The first phase of Don Bosco's experiences, I believe, may be explained in precisely the same way I have tried to explain Mr Woodcock's. The two tales are strikingly alike. One solution should be amply able to cover both.

As to his seeing the same dog twenty-seven years later (a twenty-seven-year-old dog would constitute a miracle by itself), the night was rainy and pitch dark. One shaggy big dog looks and feels pretty much like any other shaggy big dog, in the darkness, especially if his coat be drenched.

And, remember, this second dog also disappeared as soon as the lights of a town had their chance to dazzle the missionary's eyes.

Form your own conclusions as to both these canine ghost stories I've told. I have formed mine and I have expounded them to you. You don't have to agree with my deductions; unless you prefer sanity to spookiness.

I have in my desk a letter written me several years ago by a woman in Connecticut, and with it a letter from a trusted friend of mine vouching for the truthfulness and all-round reliability and good sense of the first letter's writer. The Connecticut woman told me the following odd yarn:

In her girlhood she was employed in an office that was some miles from her home. Being poor, she sought to save cash by walking to and from work. Part of the way led through an unsavory quarter of the city.

She dreaded this portion of her trip. Not in the broad daylight of morning, but in the dusk or darkness of a winter's evening. Yet she could not afford to ride. So she tried to leave the office early enough for the waning daylight to keep her safe from attack.

Then came an emergency period when all employees had to work an hour later in the afternoon. That meant night would fall before she could start for home. She was badly frightened, on the first evening of this emergency spell, as she neared the tough district.

But out of the shadows a dog appeared. Always she had been afraid of dogs. But for some reason she did not fear this one, large and fierce-looking though he was.

The animal ranged alongside. He accompanied her through the dangerous slum. At its far end, he turned back and left her.

Next evening he was there again. And he stalked

truculently at her side as before. So it went on for weeks. No rowdy dared accost a girl, thus guarded. When the month or so of late working hours was ended and she could go home in the safety of daylight, she saw the mysterious dog no more.

Day after day, morning and late afternoon, for a year or so, she passed by the spot where for so long he had waited to escort her through the danger zone. But not once did he appear. This convinced her that he had been sent miraculously to her from—*Somewhere*—to look after her in her time of need. And that he had disappeared as soon as he no longer was needed.

I did not seek to destroy her faith in the Miracle Dog's ghostliness. I wrote only saying the story was most interesting, and asking leave to use it sometime; and promising not to mention her name, nor to give any clue to her identity. She granted this permission willingly.

Then I wrote to a friend in the same town and asked for information about the woman. My friend's reply was a fine endorsement of the ghost-dog lady's repute and general character; and an assurance that the woman herself believed firmly in every word of her own narrative.

I have told the story here for what it is worth. And I believe it is 100 per cent true—as far as its actual statements are concerned. But——

Countless dogs have a psychic sense that tells them when some child or woman is frightened. Some of them play cruelly on this knowledge, to increase the fright. But infinitely more of them are stirred to the depths of their soft hearts by the human's terror, and they do all in their poor power to alleviate it.

Let us suppose a dog of the latter type was let out of its owner's house at a certain hour, for its evening exercise, and that that exercise was a ramble through the neighborhood.

The dog sees a young girl who for some unknown reason is sick with fear. She is scurrying along through the late dusk.

With the canine instinct for protecting the scared and the unhappy and the weak, the beast ranges alongside and walks with her, until instinct tells it her fear has fled. In other words, she has passed beyond the danger zone of the slum. The dog's work is done for that day, and it goes back to its own home streets.

The same thing happens next day at the same time. Thenceforward the dog always is waiting at the same spot and at the same time for the human whose guard it has constituted itself.

Of a late afternoon, weeks later, the scared human does not arrive. She has gone home an hour before the beast was let out of the house for its evening exercise. The girl, too, has been looking for the advent of the dog, but an hour too early.

Where is the ghostliness or the mystery in all that? Yet, perhaps, the woman will go to her grave pringling with the firm belief that at a hazardous crisis of her early life she was saved from possible harm—by a phantom dog. And the story may pass down, as an unquestionably true and thrilling family heirloom, to her great-grandchildren.

Of such stuff is many a so-called authentic family ghost story or epic of ancestral heroism made.

While cats—black cats—were supposed to be the everyday "familiars" of witches from earliest days, phantom black dogs were these women's guides and special demons. This was attested to, under torture, by dozens of unfortunate old dames who were brought to trial as witches. They declared Satan had appeared to them always in the form of a black dog.

It was a sweet ancient custom to attribute local evils to some half-crazed crone in the neighborhood, and to believe she had sold her soul to the devil. So she was thrown into prison and tortured horribly to make her confess. Then she was put to death.

One may imagine how much reliance was to be placed on the confessions of these unbalanced and pain-scourged old creatures; especially when they were plied with leading questions—questions which practically dictated their own answers. Under torture, and dizzy with fright, many a prisoner must have sought to save her life or to win surcease from pain by screeching *"Yes"*; when she was asked if it were not true that the Evil One had appeared to her in the semblance of a black dog and had lured her into selling her soul in return for certain supernatural powers. The testimony was worthless.

(And before we condemn too hastily these olden European abuses, let us stop to remember that in Salem and elsewhere in colonial America such trials were frequent; and that many a crazy old New England she-hermit was put to death as a witch. This with the approval and by the command of both Church and State.)

Scared night wanderers on the British moors were wont to say they saw and heard packs of ghost dogs chasing phantom deer. Such wraiths were known universally as "hell hounds" or as "devil dogs."

A brace or two of runaway hounds coursing rabbits or foxes or stags by night, and giving tongue as they struck a fresh trail—these, heard by a nervous or half-drunk human wayfarer stumbling home from the nearest pothouse, his mind bubbling with memory of spook stories—and you have a rock-solid explanation of the black hell hounds.

Anyone who has tramped the hills by night has heard the same eerie baying, and has realized that Farmer Haycock's beagle hounds have broken free from their ramshackle pen once more and are coursing rabbits. Also that they are due for a thundering good licking when they straggle home, tired and muddy and shamefaced, along about daylight. Yet this same bell-mouthed baying once awoke shudders of superstitious dread in its hearers.

Not the ignorant laity alone swallowed the yarns of phantom dogs. Men of high education believed in them. Will you let me quote an instance of this credulity? It was written by a Welsh preacher, the Rev. Edmund Jones. Jones was a Church of England clergyman and a pamphleteer. He died just before the dawn of the nineteenth century. In an exhaustive preachment on canine demonology he wrote:

"An acquaintance of mine, a man perfectly firm to tell the truth, being out at night, heard a hunting in the air, and as if they overtook something they were hunting after; and, being overtaken, made a miserable cry among them and seemed to escape; but, overtaken again, made the same dismal cry; and then escaped, and was followed after, till out of hearing."

Probably a handful of stray curs had gotten on the trail of a cat, whose yowl-punctured scratchings had forced them to retreat, every time they overhauled her. Let's cite another case from the Rev. Edmund Jones's pamphlet. Here it is:

"Mr D. W., of Pembrokeshire, a religious man and far from fear and superstition, gave me the following account: that as he was traveling by himself through a field called the Cot-moor, where two stones are set up, called The Devil's Nags, at some distance from each other, where evil spirits are said to haunt and trouble passengers, he was thrown over the hedge; and was never well afterward.

"Mr W. went with a strong fighting mastiff dog with him. But suddenly he saw another mastiff dog coming toward him. He thought to set his own dog at it. But his dog seemed much frightened and would not go near it. Mr W. stooped down to take up a stone, thinking to throw at it.

"But suddenly there came a fire around it [the phantom mastiff] so he could perceive it had a white tail and a white snip down its nose and saw its teeth grinning at him. He then knew it was one of the infernal dogs of hell; one of those dogs against which David prayeth in Psalm XXII, twentieth verse; *'Deliver . . . my darling from the power of the dog!'*"

Proving nothing that I can discern, except that

Mr W. encountered a cur, by night, which his own dog was afraid to tackle; and that the strange dog showed its resentment of stone-throwing by snarling at the man. As to the "fire around it"—heat-lightning often illumines dark objects in ghostly fashion.

Larry Trimble knew dogs as it is given to few men to know them. Thanks to his knowledge and power in dealing with them, he was able to make the first successful full-length motion picture with a canine hero. The picture was "Strongheart." It led the way for a throng of pictures along the same general line, most of them pitiably inferior to the first.

Here is a dog ghost story Trimble told me long ago at Sunnybank. He said I might print it:

He began life as a farm boy, and with an innate terror of all dogs. It was a phobia based on utter ignorance. For there were no dogs on the Trimble farm. His father was a stern disciplinarian who believed in boys working hard; and believed in punishing them heavily when they shirked.

One red-hot summer day, the father and Larry and the hired men had labored since dawn in a sun-scourged hayfield. Everyone was kept at it, without a minute's rest.

The mowing and raking and cocking of hay and its piling into a creaky wagon and then the pitching of it into a breathlessly stuffy barn loft—these be things of rare scenic beauty and of fragrance and of poetic inspiration. To all people, at least, who don't have to do it and who can watch the lovely sight from the shade of a breezy veranda. For the actual hay-harvest workers themselves—as I know by much early experience—it has not one redeeming feature. It is sizzly, unadulterated torment.

This digression, to give you city-bred readers some very faint idea what the experience meant to little Larry Trimble. He was ready to tumble over. He was dead tired. His half-grown young body ached in every joint.

In midafternoon his father sent him to the far-off farmhouse with a message, bidding him hurry back to his haying work at once. With his last available strength Larry sprinted to the house as fast as he could leg it. This haste because he had a plan which seemed just then the most wonderful in the world:

By extra speed, he could steal five minutes for a nap in the haymow before he went back to the field. And even five minutes of relaxing would be a godsend to the worn-out little boy.

To the loft he scrambled. By the time his body hit the soft hay he was asleep.

His father's voice, booming Larry's name in irate insistence from the shed beneath the loft, brought him blinkingly to his senses.

He lay there in pitch blackness. The summer afternoon had been slept away by him. The late summer night had fallen.

Meanwhile, the boy had been away from the hayfield where every available jot of rush labor was needed so sorely. Worse, he had not even done the evening chores which were his daily duty.

And now his father was after him, to find the shirking culprit and to wreak dire physical punishment. The fate of a soldier caught asleep at his post seemed almost mild, compared to what was in store for the luckless little sleeper.

Timidly and still scarcely more than half-awake, Larry mumbled a word of reply to the bellowed call of his sire. He crept to the edge of the loft and blinked down into the shed.

There was his father, a lantern in one hand and a wagon spoke in the other. Never had the boy seen him so beside himself with rage. This was due to be a beating which was likely to break every bone in Larry's skin—unless by some unexpected good luck the tough wagon spoke should break first.

His father caught sight of his white and sick scared face at the edge of the mow, and roared to him to come down. Slowly, Larry began the descent of the steep loft stairs. His legs were buckling under him. He was chattering with fright. Somehow he got to the bottom, and began to shamble sobbing toward the cleared space where his father—and the punitive wagon spoke—were awaiting him. The wagon spoke whizzed aloft as the child crawled forward to meet his doom.

(Maybe there's no scorching and eternal hell-torture waiting in the Hereafter for adults who deliberately throw dizzy panic dread and physical anguish into cringing little children. But if there is not, then I am wondering what the hell hell is for. "Woe unto him who shall offend one of these little ones!" is Christ's sternest warning.)

As Larry was halfway across the shed—— Wait, I am going to tell it in his own words to me; as closely as I can remember them. He said:

"Something thrust itself against me. *Something,* rough and big, pressed against my sweating palm. The light was too uncertain for me to see it. But I didn't need to see. I could tell by the feeling that it was a dog—a dog more than half as tall as I was.

"And I knew the dog was my friend. I knew he'd save me from that thrashing. All at once I stopped being afraid. I wasn't afraid of Dad. I wasn't afraid of this dog, though I'd always had a horror of dogs. I wasn't afraid of *anything.* I grabbed the top of the dog's head tighter with my hand, and I yelled up into Dad's face:

"'You don't dare hit me with that spoke! You'll never dare hit me again as long as you live! If you do, *he* is going to tear the throat out of you!'

"That was a lot of years ago. But I remember, as if it was yesterday, the way Dad stood gaping at me there in the lantern light. He stood that way for a long time. And I stared back at him. I wasn't afraid of him any more. I knew the dog wouldn't let him hurt me.

"Then Dad let the wagon spoke drop to the floor. He turned around without saying a word. And he went back to the house.

"Did he let me off that licking because he thought I had gone crazy from the heat? Or did he think *he* saw what *I* thought I *felt?* I'll never know. Because he never talked about it. But—he never licked me again."

So much for the earlier and more interesting part of Trimble's story. I am certain he was not lying and that he believed what he told me. The tale was true, as far as his own credence of it was concerned.

Yet I don't believe in the phantom dog. I don't believe in him at all.

The boy had been overworked, for many grueling hours that day, in the ovenlike hayfield. He had sunk into an exhaustion-drugged sleep. From this he had been roused, with a shock, to an ecstasy of mortal terror. To a delirium wherein he might well have imagined he saw or heard or felt all kinds of impossible things. And that delirium may have taken the form of a ghostly dog whose mission was to protect him from a beating.

As to his father's queer behavior—would the harshest disciplinarian have carried out his intention of thrashing the boy when he saw that the youngster was out of his head and was screeching delirious threats? I think not.

The same unwillingness to goad his delicate child into another such mania fit is enough to account for any later forbearances.

Isn't that hypothesis logical enough to explain the whole thing, without dragging a "Hound of Heaven" into the affair? Or is it?

I want to tell you the second and shorter part of Trimble's recital if I may. He told me:

"Always after that, at home or at school or with other kids, when I got into any kind of a jam that scared me stiff, I'd feel the pressure of my unseen dog's rough head under my hand. And I'd stop being afraid. I knew he'd look out for me and keep me from harm.

"As I grew older he didn't seem to be there any more. Because I didn't keep on needing him. But he came back to me, long afterward, when I was half-wild with fear—a fear that was as real to me just then as it was absurd.

"I left home, and went to New York to earn a living. I was a farm boy. It was the first time I had been in a city. The din and confusion of it 'got' me, from the instant I left the train. When I reached Broadway and Forty-second Street, people were going home from the day's work.

"Thousands of them were hustling toward me—great waves of men and women—from every direction. I had a genuine panic. I wanted to run howling away from them, before they could catch me and tear me to pieces.

"Then that great head shoved its way lovingly against my palm. And I knew I had nothing to be afraid of. Any more than I had had that night in the shed. My dog could protect me from this rushing army of people every bit as easily as he had kept me safe from Dad."

If you'll grant my first hypothesis as to Trimble's experiences, I think you'll agree with me that the same mental turmoil which had evoked the dog's presence in the shed, materialized it again at Broadway and Forty-second Street. I think the ghost, like so many others in spookology, existed only in the brain of the person who thought he saw or felt it.

Again, I may be mistaken. Lamentably often, I am prone to be.

But I am more sure of my ground in the next tale

—a tale that may once have had some actual happening on which its fantastically crooked structure was reared. A tale that has traveled down the centuries in prose and in verse and in pictorial shape.

It is a classic. As such I shall tell it. In its day it had thousands of unquestioning believers. So it merits a place here. It is the epic of the Black Dog of Newgate.

The horrendous Black Dog crops up first in British annals in the middle of the thirteenth century. It was a time of famine everywhere. A decent quantity of food was not available for even the worthiest and hardest-working Londoners. So (by decree of King Henry III, it is said) the inmates of London's Newgate Prison were skimped most drastically on rations. Quantities of them starved.

When the survivors were at their hungriest and most desperate, a black-clad man was cast into Newgate on charges of practising sorcery and witchcraft and other branches of the dreaded Black Art.

In that age, anyone who did seemingly impossible deeds, that called on inventiveness, was in grave danger of apprehension as a sorcerer. Especially if he dabbled in chemistry. Edison and Alexander Graham Bell and Madame Curie, and other modern immortals who have wrought scientific miracles, would never have passed the first stages of their researches, without going to prison or to death, if they had had the misfortune to be born a few centuries earlier.

Thus, the black-clad man who was jailed at Newgate on a sorcery charge, during the thirteenth-century famine, may have been a harmless inventor—or at worst a fortune teller or other charlatan. But whatever his offense, his punishment was pretty ghastly. Not at the hands of the state, but of his fellow convicts.

The prisoners had great sympathy with murderers and thieves and the like. But nobody had any sympathy at all with a sorcerer. He was better dead than living. Besides, they themselves were perishing from famine.

So they slew the man in black. Then they cooked him and ate him.

Before he died he promised them that a dreadful curse would descend on them; by way of vengeance for his murder. And when a sorcerer called down a curse as blighting as that, it was a thing to be feared.

But the convicts' appetites were keener than their superstitious awe. So they braved the curse. And they killed and ate the curser.

To this point the story is fairly well authenticated, by records of the time and of a few years later. Now for the ghostly part of it:

Their hunger satisfied, the prisoners began to remember the curse and to wax more and more worried. Their worry was fanned to wild horror on that same day.

A black-clad man carrying a broom passed through the courtyard. (Probably a scavenger or one of the prison sweepers—a new employee, it may be assumed, since none of the convicts recognized him.)

The slayers recalled that their victim had worn black, as did this newcomer. Also the latter was brandishing a broom. And broomsticks ever were the time-dishonored accessories of conjurors and witches and sorcerers.

Scarcely had the sable-dressed sweeper passed out of sight around a corner of the wall, when from the same direction a sinister jet-black dog trotted toward the goggle-eyed onlookers.

So immediately did the dog appear after the departure of the man with the broom, that some of the hunger-dazed and superstitious prisoners vowed they saw the man change himself into the dog. The tale swept through all the prison; along with the tale of the promised curse. That was quite enough. The Black Dog of Newgate had come into existence.

And his sinister presence was to remain there, in or out of the body, for several centuries.

Story followed grisly story: of his actions and demoniac powers. The tales lost no flesh in the retelling.

The Black Dog, in all likelihood, was one of the myriad stray curs of the London streets, and he had strolled into the prison confines in quest of shelter or for mouldy food scraps or bones. Either he liked the place or else his canine vanity was stirred by the flattering excitement caused by his advent.

For he decided to continue his visits to the jail at various intervals. And each of his arrivals within the walls was the occasion of new panic and of new tall stories.

By chance, the Black Dog prowled the prison yard one night just before an execution. Henceforth, it was said he came there on the eve of every hanging, to drag away the soul of the condemned felon.

That was but one of a score of legends which thickened around him as the years went by.

But let's go back to the moment when the broom-wielding man in black went around the corner of the courtyard wall, and the Black Dog appeared there instantly in his place; the apparition that made prisoners swear they had seen the man transform himself magically into the demon hound which was sent by the devoured sorcerer to destroy his killers.

A group of prisoners were so crazed by horror at the sight that they hurled themselves at the jail gates, braving the swords and pikes of the guards stationed there, sooner than remain in the Black Dog's fatal presence.

Some of the fugitives were struck down by the guard. But the assault upon the gate was so sudden that a handful of them buffeted their way through to the streets and thence to the security of the wild country beyond.

According to one of the numberless legends, the Black Dog followed the successful jail breakers singly, and dragged them down to hideous death.

Luke Hutton, a seventeenth-century pamphleteer who dug up all the Black Dog information, false or true, that he could find in ancient records and broadsheets, explains thus the tracking and the seizing of the escaped Newgate prisoners:

"The Black Dog is a black conscience, haunting none but black-conditioned people, such as Newgate may challenge to be guests."

Having made his way into the prison, and finding the place and its terrified inmates amusing, the Black

Dog added to his awful repute by trotting somberly alongside the carts which took condemned folk to Tyburn Hill to be hanged.

Forgetting the normal fact that dogs always had loved to escort carts and carriages on any journey at all, this escort duty self-imposed by the Black Dog took on a new and horrible significance in the eyes of believers. They were certain he accompanied the carts to the gallows to grab the escaping souls of the hanged.

It was of this superstition that a pious balladmonger wrote in one of the many jingled broadsheets of his era:

Have thou no doubt but Time shall set thee free.
And yet hereafter learn thee to beware
Of this Black Dog, and do his dangers flee.
Give others warning, lest this fall their share.
Say to the world, when thou art freed from hell,
Newgate's Black Dog thou sawest; and knewest too well.

I have spoken of Luke Hutton's booklet; into which the compiler crowded all the Black Dog material he could find. It bore this imposing title:

The Discovery of a London Monster Called
THE BLACK DOG OF NEWGATE
Profitable For All to Take Heed by.

Hutton did not seem to "take heed by" the moral lesson of his own book. For, it is said, he lived a lurid life which landed him in Newgate; and last of all on the gallows of Tyburn Hill.

In one of my reference books I have a reproduction of a woodcut of the demon canine. He is depicted as nearly as tall as the Statue of Liberty. So tall that his snake-crowned head rises higher than Newgate's uppermost tier of cells. He carries a huge iron chain around his neck and he is staring down malignantly at a wretched prisoner who cowers in the barred window of one of the upper cells. The picture's caption is:

"*Vidé, Legé, Cavé*. [See, read, beware.]" "Time Bringeth All Things to Light." Printed at London by M. P. for Robert Wilson at his shop at Grayes-Inne Gate in Holborne, 1638."

Let me end this ghostless-ghostful chapter of our book by a jump from old-time England to twentieth-century Sunnybank, and to a mercifully short recital of a tale I have told at least twice and to greater length elsewhere.

It is the saga of our only Sunnybank ghost. And, naturally enough, that ghost was a dog's.

I'll admit I find it less easy to explain on gross material grounds the incidents of this yarn than those of any of its predecessors I have cited. But I believe there may be a wholly normal solution of the whole occurrence, if only I had the intelligence to work it out. Which I confess I have not. At least, not in all details.

I shall preface the account by saying I am not on record as making any personal statements concerning it. Nor shall I speak of anything I myself may have seen or may have imagined I saw. The whole story shall be a matter of proven record—as far as it goes. As for explanation—as I told you, I have none yet which seems convincing, even to myself. But there must be one. Here goes:

I had a crossbreed dog, Rex by name. He was larger than my collies. He was fawn-colored and shorthaired, and he had an odd-shaped scar across his forehead. He was slavishly devoted to me. Hours at a time, in the evening, he would lie at my feet, looking up at my face. If I moved to any other part of the room or of the porch, he would follow me unobtrusively, and lie down again at my feet and continue to gaze up at me.

He was not allowed in the dining room. So at mealtimes he stood on the veranda just outside the long french window, statuelike in his lack of motion and staring in at me, where I sat at the table with my back to the window.

He was not allowed in my study. So, when I was working there, he lay, daily, for years, on a hallway rug in front of the door.

I beg you to bear in mind the uninteresting details I have been setting forth. They are vital elements in the less dull part of my story, which follows.

In March of 1916 Rex was killed. (Those of you who have read my *Lad: A Dog* may recall how and why Rex died.)

Henry A. Healy and his pretty wife spent an autumn evening with us in 1917, more than a year and a half after Rex's death. Healy, by the way, was a brilliant and a cool-headed financier, one of the highest officials of the so-called Leather Trust. Not a visionary, nor addicted to practical jokes; nor fanciful in any way.

We spent a lazily pleasant evening in front of the living-room fire, he and I. As he was on his way to his car, he said, rather wistfully:

"Bert, I wish there were some one or some thing on earth that adored me as Rex worships you. I was watching him all evening. He lay there at your feet the whole time, looking up at you; as a devotee might look up to its god. I wish——"

"Good Lord, man!" I interrupted, sputtering in crass astonishment. "Rex has been dead for more than eighteen months. You know that. I told you all about it at the time."

Healy's strong face went blank for a moment.

"Why!" he said, dazed. "Why, so he has! I—I remember, now. Just the same," he continued stubbornly, "I can swear he was lying there at your feet and looking up at you all this evening. Just as I've seen him lie there ever since he was a puppy."

None of the living Sunnybank dogs—and no dog at all that *I* am prepared to say I saw—had been lying in front of the living-room fire or anywhere else in the room, that evening. So it is not likely Healy confused a live long-coated collie for a dead shorthaired crossbreed.

Also, Healy was an old friend of my living dogs; as well as of myself. He knew them all, too well to mistake one of them for Rex.

Make what you can of it. It puzzles me to this day.

In the summer of 1918 my lifelong friend, the Rev. Appleton Grannis (who is now rector of St Anne's

Church at Lowell, Mass.) came to visit us. He had been in the West for some years. This was his first Sunnybank visit since his return.

Grannis never had seen Rex; never had heard of him. Nor did Grannis and Healy know each other. Neither of them had so much as heard of the other.

One afternoon Grannis and I were sitting for an hour or so in the dining room, I with my back as usual to the french window, he facing me. We were chatting of old times, and trying to counteract the heat with cold beer. When we got up to leave the room he said:

"I thought I knew the Sunnybank dogs. I thought they were all collies."

"They are," I told him.

"Then what dog was it," he asked me, "that has been standing all afternoon on the porch, there, looking in through the long window at you? He is big and fawn-colored, and he is short-haired and he has a scar on his forehead. Which dog is he?"

With absolute truthfulness I made answer:

"I don't know!"

Bruce, most beautiful of all our collies, had a queerly psychic strain. He alone used to be permitted to come into my study and to sprawl there while I was writing. Naturally, he had entered the study across the small rug in front of its door—the rug which had been Rex's chosen resting place during my work hours in there.

Not once, from the day of Rex's killing, did Bruce step on that rug. Always, to the end of his life, he skirted it carefully, as though he were walking around some dog or some other object which was lying there.

This can be verified by many a Sunnybank guest, still living, whose attention I called to Bruce's puzzling avoidance of the empty rug.

Not a thrillingly interesting yarn, is it? Yet the truth of every statement in it can be proven past doubt.

And somewhere, perhaps, there is a simple and normal and logical explanation for it all. I believe there is. But I lack the brains to discover it.

So much for our chapter on canine ghosts—or canine pseudo-ghosts. A drearily fruitless theme at best. I'm glad we've finished with it. Aren't *you?*

CHAPTER VIII

Dogs Behind the Footlights

I WAS FOUR YEARS OLD when I saw my first stage dog.

He was one of the many thousand little dogs which successively and successfully have enacted the same strenuous role in the same play, for hundreds of years. Certainly since the beginning of the seventeenth century; probably much earlier.

The play is *Punch and Judy*.

One of its chief characters is a dog named Toby.

There is no way of guessing even remotely how many small dogs have played that exacting role. For there are no statistics to tell how many *Punch-and-Judy* shows have tramped the dusty roads of Great Britain and of Continental Europe; and have set up their miniature stages in market places and on street corners and in halls and homes, during all these thirty-odd decades.

But it is safe to say that each of the numberless tiny theater troupes included a Toby. And, to play Toby, a dog must be a natural actor; and he or she must take a certain vainglorious pride in artistry of performance. Fifty thousand Tobys, since *Punch and Judy* first took the road, probably is a gross understatement.

Fifty thousand first-rate super-competent canine

actors; most of them giving nine or ten performances or more per day, six or seven days a week, fifty-two weeks a year, throughout their entire careers!

I was privileged to see my first *Punch-and-Judy* show on the beach at Brighton, England; and to see my latest (I hope not my last) enactment of that sterling classic drama on a Haymarket street corner, in London, more than a half-century afterward.

At the Brighton show, when I was a very small child, I watched the performance, goggle-eyed and breathless. If I could get the same kick out of any play, nowadays, I would be willing to spend a month's earnings for a single ticket. (And I suppose I would have to pay out a still larger sum, next day, to a heart specialist or a nerve healer.)

In all my four long years of life, never had I been so stirred up as at the Brighton show. Far less by Punch's wholesale villainies and by Judy's sufferings than by the marvelous acting of Toby. To me, that first Toby of my experience was a sublime dog. I wanted to pick him up and to squeeze him; from sheer admiration. And I followed my impulse.

I trailed along, mesmerized, in the wake of the troupe, as it went to its next stopping point on the crowded beach. There, while the stage was set up, I grabbed the apathetically resting Toby in my short arms and hugged him. I told him, the while, what a grand dog he was.

He had all the highstrung actor's temperament, it seems, with none of an actor's craving for praise. For he rewarded my hug and my babbled adulation by nipping me right painfully on the nose.

DOGS BEHIND THE FOOTLIGHTS

It was my earliest experience with the stark difference between the artistic and the personal side of actor nature.

When and how *Punch and Judy* was written first, I don't know. Nobody knows. Perhaps it was not written at all, in its accepted form, till the 1850's, but was learned and adapted by word of mouth. For I have heard at least a dozen variations on its dialogue.

I have read that its original form dates back to the era of early religious drama, and that it began life as a Morality Play. Therein, Punch represented Mankind in its life battle between good and evil.

As with Dr Faustus, he was haunted by a black dog which tempted him to various wrong or unwise deeds. His struggles with the devil dog took the form of beatings and of lively scrimmages. This horseplay so delighted the medieval audiences that the dog's part in it was built up and added to and presently was made all-important.

Thus was the character of Toby evolved; having traveled a long way from the original.

In 1854 or 1855, some scholar (whose name I have forgotten, if ever I knew it) undertook to standardize the immortal puppet play by having a supposedly accepted version of it printed in England, under the modest title of *The Wonderful Drama of Punch and Judy and the Little Dog TOBY.*" In that standardization, the stage directions call specifically for Toby to bite Punch's nose at least three times.

So perhaps the Toby at Brighton did not nip my nose from resentment at my hug and my incoherent praise of his work, but simply by way of rehearsal. I should like to think so. For the physical hurt was grievous. And the hurt to my trust in the friendliness of all the world was even sharper.

Toby, by the way, is the only living actor in any *Punch-and-Judy* show. The other characters are puppets, manipulated from below. For some obscure reason, all the Tobies I have seen wore enormous paper ruffs around their necks. I have heard that this dates back to the early Italian past and that it is borrowed from a detail of the conventional Punchinello costume.

But stage dogs go back much further in dramatic history than the earliest *Punch-and-Judy* era. The Roman emperor, Vespasian, in 78 A.D., shouted with delight at the acting of a dog named Sopicos. This animal, imported from Greece, took a leading part in one of the amphitheater plays.

In the course of the action, Sopicos was supposed to be mortally injured. He went through a thrilling death scene, then crumpled in a heap in mid-stage, shivering, and gradually relaxing his muscles in death.

Lest the spectators be overly saddened by the fate of so fine an actor, Sopicos sprang presently to his feet, after he had breathed his last; and he went through an intricate dance on his hind legs.

Then there was the familiar "Dog of Montargis." A play was made from his exploits: a drama revived again and again throughout the years. The dog himself was its chief character. For on him hung the whole plot.

The role was exacting. It could be ruined, and the

play along with it, if it were not entrusted to a canine artist whose perfect performance could be relied on.

Probably you are familiar with the true story of the Dog of Montargis; the strange tale on which the play long afterward was built. Here it is. It is worth retelling.

In the reign of Charles Fifth of France—"Charles the Wise"—a young captain of the Guard, Aubrey de Montdidier, fell in love with a lady-in-waiting, Isabelle de Villenomble. His foremost rival for her hand was another officer of the Royal Guard, one Captain Macaire.

Isabelle chose Aubrey. Macaire vowed revenge. But it was not easy to take that revenge.

Not only was Montdidier a better swordsman than Macaire, but he had a four-legged comrade which was even more redoubtable than was his sword. That defender was Aubrey's magnificent staghound, Dragon.

Dragon was Montdidier's best friend. He had all a true staghound's deathless love for his master. He was Aubrey's constant bodyguard, at home and at barracks and in court. There seemed scant chance for Macaire to break through the dog's unsleeping vigilance.

But Macaire's long-awaited opportunity came at last, in the autumn of 1361. Aubrey de Montdidier was riding through the dense forest of Bondy. Dragon was cantering gaily in front of him. As the hound passed by a bend in the road and momentarily out of his master's sight, a hand reached forth from a thicket: a hand gripping a rock.

The rock descended crashingly on the dog's skull, stunning him.

In Dragon's wake, the unsuspecting Aubrey rode around the bend. The dog's assailant sprang from the thicket behind him and stabbed him through the heart.

Then he hauled his victim's body into the woods and buried it. He made his escape long before Dragon came shakily to his senses from the rock blow.

The dog cast about the trampled ground. At once he struck his master's trail. He followed it unerringly to the newdug grave, cunningly hidden under a riffle of forest leaves. There he stood guard for two days and nights, trying to bring human aid by howling incessantly.

But the peasants who heard that unearthly series of death howls crossed themselves and prayed for divine protection against the werewolf; and they stayed as far as possible from that part of the forest.

When Dragon realized nobody would respond to his howls for help, he galloped to near-by Paris, to the town house of Isabelle de Villenomble. There he set up such a frightful din that the servants tried to drive him from the door. But Isabelle looked from a window, and saw and recognized him.

She ran down, to order that he be admitted to the house. Dragon seized her by the hem of her robe, and began pulling her out into the street. Isabelle seems to have understood dog nature. Also, she was well acquainted with Dragon. And she wondered to see him absent from his master. Never before had she known the hound to go anywhere without young Montdidier.

THE ROCK DESCENDED CRASHINGLY ON THE DOG'S HEAD

DOGS BEHIND THE FOOTLIGHTS 207

She told two of her menservants to come along with her, as guards. She followed Dragon, as he kept running a short distance ahead and then waiting for her to catch up with him. The dog was in very evident unhappiness and excitement.

Out of Paris and along the dusty rutted road the little procession moved until it had arrived at the fringe of the forest of Bondy. Still the hound kept on. Still, guided by the dog and by a womanly intuition, Isabelle followed. Then Dragon left the road, at a bend, and plunged into the thick of the woods.

Presently he halted, and again his death howl split the forest silences. Following, Isabelle and her menservants found the dog standing above a mound of recently turned earth, whence he had scraped the screen of dead leaves. At Isabelle's command, the two men began to dig, with their broad-bladed knives and with their hooked fingers.

The shallowly buried body of young Aubrey de Montdidier was exhumed.

When the law had taken charge of the matter, Dragon went to Isabelle's Paris house to live. He was heartbroken. Yet he accepted his dead master's sweetheart as his new owner.

Captain Macaire, at the head of his company, came marching, one day, down a street where Isabelle and Dragon were strolling. At sight of Macaire, the hound yelled in sudden fury and hurled himself at the captain. The soldiers had much difficulty in pulling him away from their commander.

The story spread through Paris. It came to the ears of the king himself, along with the tale that Macaire had been Montdidier's unsuccessful rival in love and that he had sworn revenge.

King Charles sent for Macaire, and bade him hide behind a group of courtiers in the throne room of the palace. Then he told Isabelle to bring the great hound into the room by the farthest doorway.

Into the royal presence came Dragon, stalking majestically beside his new mistress. This, until he was midway across the apartment. Then he paused, sniffing the air of the place with upraised nostrils.

Only for a moment he stood so. Then, snarling, he clove his way through the clump of courtiers, straight to Macaire, and leaped for the captain's throat, bearing him to the floor. As before, he was dragged away.

But the king had seen the death hate the hound felt toward Macaire. He was told, also, that up to the time of Montdidier's murder, Dragon had not molested the captain; nor paid any heed at all to him. For those rough-and-ready times, that was evidence enough to cause Macaire's arrest, even if only on the accusing testimony of a dog.

According to medieval French law, the accused had the privilege of meeting his accuser in mortal combat: a combat fantastically known in olden law books as "God's Judgment," because of the belief that the Almighty would bring victory to the innocent.

Therefore, the Chevalier Macaire was told he must meet his accuser, the dog, Dragon, in an improvised arena, on the Ile Notre Dame, in the Seine; there to fight for his life and to prove his innocence.

All the court and thousands of townsfolk crowded into the amphitheater on the day set for the combat.

DOGS BEHIND THE FOOTLIGHTS 209

By royal decree, Macaire was allowed to carry a heavy iron-studded club by way of weapon. This against the rending teeth of the hound.

For, unarmed, Man is the weakest and most defenceless creature—for his size—in all the animal kingdom. And the Dog is practically the only member of the animal kingdom with but one set of weapons: his jaws. Almost everything else, from man to mouse, has five sets of weapons: jaws and four limbs. But the dog does not use his claws or feet or legs for offensive purposes in battle. He has his teeth-lined jaws, alone.

After much deliberation, it was deemed that Macaire's iron-studded bludgeon would offset—or more than offset—Dragon's teeth.

The signal for battle was given. Macaire swung his studded club aloft and advanced warily upon his foe. Dragon was released by the two attendants who had been assigned to hold him until word was given that the fight was on.

Across the small arena, with the speed and deadliness of a flung spear, the hound dashed toward his master's killer. Macaire stopped, and stood awaiting the brute's charge. Dragon leaped for Macaire's throat.

Down came the murderous club, well aimed and driven by all the force and skill of a desperate man. If it had reached Dragon's head, it would have been tenfold more deadly than had been the rock that smote him in the forest of Bondy.

But it did not reach the dog's head.

Almost in mid-air, Dragon shifted his body as he charged. As lithely as a cat and with a born fighter's innate judging of distance and of direction, he dodged the smashing blow of the club.

Before the bludgeon could be swung upward for another blow—before Macaire could recover his stance or his balance—the hound had flashed in and had him by the throat.

To the earth sprawled Macaire, under that fearful impact, the great dog ripping away at his jugular; the club flying from the man's fist as its wielder subconsciously threw out his arms to recover his balance.

The stewards and the heralds-at-arms rushed in. The hound was dragged away from his half-crazed victim. Blubberingly, his nerve gone and his superstitious dread aroused, Macaire stammered forth a confession of his crime.

From the arena the murderer was led to the gallows. There, in due and ancient form, he was hanged.

So much for the actual tale of Dragon and of Aubrey de Montdidier and of Isabelle de Villenomble and of the Chevalier Macaire. Apparently, it is true in all its main details. What followed may be truth or it may be legend. It is fairly well authenticated—for a yarn of that blurredly distant age:

It is said that Isabelle had Montdidier's body interred in a chapel expressly built for him; that she died of grief, less than a year later, and was buried at his side; and that the tomb, by her ante-mortem orders, was sealed. Also that a later owner of the estate caused the tomb to be opened, and that the skeleton of a giant staghound was discovered stretched above the two graves.

Well, you can see for yourselves what gorgeous fat

material the story contained for one of the good old-time blood-and-thunder medieval melodramas. Also that the play's success hinged on the perfect acting of the dog himself.

In France it was dramatized, long before ever it was acted in English. And it made fortune and fame for its author—thanks to the spectacular performance of the dog that played the role of Dragon.

In 1814, it was translated into English and was entitled *The Dog of Montargis; or The Forest of Bondy*. Then came a hitch. How was a dog to be taught to plunge at Macaire's throat and to try to tear it open? How had it been done in France?

I don't know how the various successive Continental companies had achieved that effect. But in England (where the drama had its debut at Covent Garden a year before the Battle of Waterloo), the problem was solved in a very simple way.

The trained dog, chosen to play Dragon, was inordinately fond of sausages. He was taught, during rehearsals, that the actor playing Macaire always had a string of lusciously greasy sausages hidden inside his neckcloth in the duel scene. Then the dog was kept hungry for many hours before the curtain was to go up.

At scent of the sausages, he would hurl himself on Macaire with seemingly ferocious intent, and would rend the man's neckerchief in an industrious sausage hunt.

The play had a phenomenal run at Covent Garden. It was revived again and again during the twenty years that followed.

The Dog of Montargis was translated into German too. A popular actor, Karsten by name, was engaged to play Macaire. A trick dog was hired from its owner, for the role of Dragon. Then came a hitch.

The poet-philosopher, Goethe, was impresario at the Weimar Theater where the drama was to open. Goethe detested all dogs. (In his *Faust* he makes the devil take the form of a dog, and he uses up many lines of poetic monologue in cursing the beast.) Moreover, Goethe had a deep reverence for the sacredness of dramatic art and a jealous regard for the quality of every actor who planned to play at Weimar.

When he heard a trick dog was to enact the star role there, he put up a sign over the stage door, reading *"No Dogs Admitted."* Then he appealed to the authorities to forbid the desecration.

His plea was rejected. Whereat, Goethe resigned fumingly from his position as director of the Weimar Theater.

By far the best of the canine actors I have had the good fortune to see was the rightly termed "wonder dog," Jasper.

Jasper was a friend of mine. One evening I was booked to speak at a rather large dinner. Jasper was to be brought thither by his master to go through his amazing stunts after the close of the more formal proceedings.

On my way to the banqueting room, I saw the dog and his master sitting patiently on some backstairs, waiting to be called in to entertain the guests. I sat down on the stairs beside them.

We three had a great evening together. It was a case of "deep calling unto deep." I don't know when I have had a more interesting time. Jasper enjoyed it, too, immensely. So did his master. The upshot of it was that all three of us forgot about the drearily formal dinner on the floor below. And by the time we remembered we were supposed to take an active part in it, it was over.

Thus I was spared the miseries of a public banquet and the guests were spared the greater misery of a Terhune after-dinner speech. But everyone except myself was the loser by Jasper's failure to appear.

It was at about this time that Jasper was drafted to take an infinitely appealing part in a play called *Young America,* which was to be produced in New York. The play itself amounted to little enough. But Jasper's genius kept it going long after otherwise it must have closed.

He played the role of the boy-hero's chum dog.

In that capacity, he had to fly murderously at a policeman (enacted by his own master) who came to arrest the boy. He had to hurl himself screaming against the locked door over whose threshold the lad had been dragged by the police.

He lay limp and apparently lifeless when a motorcar was supposed to have hit him and when he was carried onto the stage after the accident.

But, to me, the best part of his long and glorious performance in the play—as well as in the evening I spent making friends with him and with his trainer on the stairs above the banquet hall—was the calm and *human* poise he maintained when he was not on duty.

It was as though some wise and well-controlled man were going through the work.

There was a nameless human quality—a strain of super-intelligence—I never encountered before or since in my association with any dog. I can't describe it. But myriads of people who saw the play, *Young America,* will bear me out in what I say of his strange superiority of brain.

In fact, Jasper had a hundred times too much brain. And that is what struck him dead while he still was in his early prime. The world was robbed prematurely of an intellect which, given longer time and better conditions, might have bridged much of the wide chasm between man and beast.

Jasper was not much to look at. A blend of bull terrier and of fox terrier, if I remember aright. Grayish and whitish, short-coated; unassuming. But one of the greatest dogs, mentally, in the history of the world. And by far the greatest canine actor. I can't forget his performance, even after all these years. He was a Personality. He was infinitely more: An Impossibility.

He was more than a dog. I—well, I don't know *what* he was. Whatever it may have been, it was too much for him. And his too-great brain killed him, from meningitis. It was as though God did not wish us humans to probe into that nebulous borderland which separates Man from Beast.

Let's get our feet back on more normal ground, shan't we?

Charles Hawtrey, the British comedian, owned a smooth-haired fox terrier who played a slight part in one of Hawtrey's farces. His chief job was to emerge from under a sofa at the opening of the second act of the show—to crawl out, as if from sleep, and to stretch and yawn prodigiously; and then to trot over to Hawtrey to be petted.

One morning, in the mid-run of the play in London, a dog thief grabbed the terrier during the four-legged actor's daily walk through the Green Park. The crook knew how all-important was the dog's brief bit of acting to the play's success. He planned to hold him a few days, then to open wily cash negotiations for his return.

All morning, Hawtrey and his associates hunted in vain for the missing terrier on whose presence the play depended. Then, when they failed to find him, an employee of the theater told Hawtrey he had an unusually talented spaniel which could play the part after a single rehearsal.

The spaniel was sent for, in a rush. He arrived, plump and truculent, yet biddable. Throughout the afternoon and until the hour for the curtain, he was rehearsed; over and over. He was ready at last to give a smooth performance.

When the second act's curtain rose, the spaniel crawled out from under the couch and stretched himself and yawned, according to his intensive training. Then there was a scurry of scampering paws, offstage.

The terrier's keen incisor teeth had scissored the rope which bound him to a post in the thief's home. Free, he had scampered at top speed for the theater. He flashed between the legs of the doorman and into the playhouse.

He rushed onto the stage, just in time to see another and wholly strange dog get the laugh which always had been his: for the stretching and the yawning and the leisurely advance toward Hawtrey.

Red rage encompassed him at the sight of this wretched interloper and at sound of the audience's multiple titter. He flew at the spaniel which was stealing his thunder.

The spaniel, not at all averse to battle at any time or place, whizzed about, midway in his approach to Hawtrey, and met the terrier's whirlwind attack.

There, all over the stage, from center to left, from left to right, from backdrop to footlights, waged a mightily vehement dog fight, to the vast delight of the spectators; until the curtain was signaled to drop in much haste on the unadvertised scene of carnage.

There was another and more renowned British actor whose small dog became part of contemporary stage history. The mite of a dog was Fussy, Sir Henry Irving's immortal and quite worthless fox terrier.

Fussy had no designated part in any of the Irving plays. But he had a passion for slipping out of the actor's dressing room and pattering joyously into the glare of the footlights—preferably in such moments as the *Hamlet* soliloquy or the Walpurgis Night scene in *Faust*.

Irving was aloof and grim and sardonic toward mankind at large. But he was helplessly malleable in anything or everything which concerned worthless little Fussy.

He might—and *did*—drop one or more of his leading actors and actresses from their parts for the slightest digression from his martinet teachings (as when he kicked Conway out of the role of Faust at an hour's notice in 1887 and substituted George Alexander in the part; demoting Conway to the playing of Valentine). But Fussy was at liberty—on and off stage—to do whatever the dog might choose to do.

Across the stage he might romp, at will. And behind the scenes and in Irving's home the terrier reigned supreme. Fussy was the one soft spot in Irving's otherwise adamant armor against the world.

To substantiate this—though in my youth it was too well known in the theatrical world to need confirming—I would like to quote a paragraph or two, if I may, from W. G. Robertson's book of reminiscences, *Time Was:*

"All the intimacy that Irving withheld from mankind he lavished upon dogs. Or perhaps latterly on *a* dog. It was the link between him and humanity.

"Fussy originally had belonged to Ellen Terry. But Irving won his heart through his stomach (he was a greedy dog!) and Fussy gradually became his property. Or, more correctly, Irving became Fussy's property.

"On one terrible occasion, when the Lyceum Company was going to America, Fussy, starting with his master, was left behind at Southampton. Days later, he turned up, dirty and footsore, at the Lyceum Theater (then in the hands of Mary Anderson) and was of course recognized and received with due reverence by Barry, the stage doorkeeper.

"Irving thought Fussy must have found his way back to London by following the railroad lines. The theory was confirmed when, on a later American tour, Fussy was again left behind, this time at a New York railway station, when the company set out for San Francisco.

"His master discovered the loss almost at once, and the train was halted. A small white object came in sight, plodding steadily along the line. Fussy had started out for California!"

"Fritz" (J.K.) Emmett, premier music comedian of my boyhood, owned a splendid St Bernard. To the dog, Emmett's plays owed a goodly portion of their success. Not that the St Bernard had any important or significant work to do in these comedies.

But he walked onto the stage with his master in many a scene. There he comported himself as should any other stately and well-educated dog of his grand breed.

At times he would follow Emmett from one side of the stage to the other or to the footlights; moving with massive dignity and perfect self-assurance. Again, he would lie down at his master's feet for a nap.

It is reported that one of these naps ruined the rendition of a sentimental yodel ballad Emmett was singing. For, at a pianissimo passage in the song, a raucous canine snore ripped its way through the tender melody, with grisly effect.

It "stopped the show" for more than a minute, while the star and the orchestra and the audience bawled with Homeric laughter. The sweetly sentimental mood of the scene was shattered beyond immediate recall.

Instead of losing his temper at the wreck of his song, Emmett laughed more delightedly than did anyone else. Stooping, he rumpled the snoring dog's ears in rough affection, shouting cheerfully:

"Wake up, old chap! This is a solo. It isn't a duet."

There are managers and stars who won't allow a dog on the stage. They claim its presence takes the audience's attention away from the actors and the action. I have seen several cases where this has been proven most conclusively. But chiefly when the dog forgets he is supposed to be a mere lay figure and behaves like a dog. For one or two examples:

Guy Bates Post, in *The Masqueraders,* was discovered at the rise of the second-act curtain seated writing at a table in his shabby sitting room. On the floor, in the center of the stage, lay his faithful police dog, the pathetic hero's one friend in a cruel world.

On the night I saw the show, the effect of sad loneliness was lightened a bit in mid-scene. The police dog was young and he was playful and he was bored by the dullness of his surroundings.

So he rolled over and over, kicking all four legs high in air, and coaxing Bates, by jolly rumbling sounds, to come and romp with him. Until the dog left the stage, the audience continued to giggle at his antics and to focus its attention on him instead of concentrating on the play.

Again, when Arnold Daly was playing in Shaw's *General John Regan,* his white bull terrier, Rover, was on the stage much of the time; as a recognized member of the cast.

In a scene where arrangements are made for a patriotic celebration, one Mary Ellen, a decidedly grimy colleen, is chosen to depict an Irish fairy. Someone objects that she is not overclean in appearance. Dr O'Grady (played by Arnold Daly) answers that they can wash her.

Just then, at the performance I attended, Rover started up from a snooze on the floor and began to scratch himself with a violence that jarred the stage. He threw all his muscular energy into an effort to annihilate the flea whose stinging bite had awakened him. As the audience began to titter, Arnold Daly improvised a line to cover the situation:

"Yes," he announced, "we can wash Mary Ellen. And while we are about it we'd better wash Rover too."

Many of his hearers, witnessing the play for the first time, thought the flea-scratching was a part of the prearranged stage business. The attention-destroying titter died down at once, and the scene was saved.

When Katharine Cornell starred in *The Barretts of Wimpole Street* a few years ago, a biscuit-colored cocker spaniel was bought and was put through a course of intensive training—or rehearsing—to enact Elizabeth's pet dog, Flush.

I saw the play during the earliest part of its long run. At that matinee Flush did all sorts of distracting and destructive things to mess up the poetic beauty of the great love scene between Elizabeth and Browning.

Elizabeth, an invalid, reclined on a couch while her suitor bent tenderly above her. At the other end of the couch lay her spaniel. For a few minutes Flush behaved decorously, as he had been taught to. Then, palpably, he found the whole thing stupid, and he sought for ways to amuse himself.

Miss Cornell's fingers were hanging gracefully over the side of the couch. Flush glared at them as though they were the most dramatically thrilling objects in all his experience. First he tried to scare them by growling threateningly. Then he made little abortive charges at them.

Then he seized one of them in his mouth and bit it softly, passing on to the next finger and to the next. Miss Cornell shifted the position of her hand, and the fascinating fingers were out of the spaniel's reach. So Flush looked around in search of some new thing to attack.

He found it. It was the curved corner of the couch. This offending upholstered knob he bit and gnawed and growled over, with much relish.

But soon he wearied of assailing so unresponsive a foe. And he seemed to realize for the first time that there were a lot of giggling people on the far side of the footlights.

He turned over on his back, his fluffy paws gesticulating gaily; and still upside down, he rolled his eyes in mock ferocity at the overjoyed audience.

All this time, mind you, a love scene of rare beauty and fervor was in progress between Elizabeth and Browning: a scene which was the foundation stone of all the rest of the play. And how many people were centering their minds on it? How many, instead, were grinning at the spaniel's foolery and wondering what next he would do?

As I say, that was almost at the start of the play's run. People who saw it later on told me Flush settled down to perfect decorum, not to say sluggishness. That he had lost all his puppylike bumptiousness. That he lay sleepily on the couch and made no effort to entertain himself during the long scene.

It was rumored that a shot of dope was given him just before performances; to keep him from stealing the show, as at first. This report was denied most vigorously by the management and by Miss Cornell.

It was a suspicion not likely to enhance the play's success. A drugged dog is not a pleasant sight. The belief that a dog lies quiescent on the stage, only because his senses have been befogged by dope, would not popularize any show. Small wonder the story was denied so emphatically! Yet a doctor said to me:

"The denials probably are true. Just the same—if ever I saw an animal display what looked like symptoms of mild drugging, that animal was Flush."

Once at a performance of *The Huguenots,* at the old Manhattan Opera House, I saw a cat strut across the stage. The audience was convulsed. Why? The spectacle of a cat walking along a street or across a room would not provoke the weakest smile; nor indeed any interest at all.

The snoring of Emmett's St Bernard; the flea-scratching of Arnold Daly's bull terrier; the back-rolling and grumblings of Guy Bates Post's police dog; Flush's gentle attempts at self-entertainment—none of these would have raised a laugh, if they had occurred anywhere else than in a theater.

Why were they good for wholesale amusement on the part of audiences who had paid hard cash to see something wholly different? Even the most inveterate theatergoer would have scoffed at the idea of paying from $1.50 to $4 for the privilege of going to see a dog scratch fleas or nibble playfully at an actress' fingers.

There must be a theory to account for it. But I don't know what it is. Do you?

By the way, in this chapter on dogs behind the footlights, I have not touched on the "Animal Acts" of vaudeville. Partly because I think of the dogs in those acts as Victims, not as Actors. Partly because I leave the theater when an animal act is put on.

I am told that some of the wretched trick dogs have been trained by kindness. I can't prove this is not true. But hundreds of them have learned their tricks after long weeks of right damnable cruelty. So I don't care to stay and watch them go through their tragic repertory.

CHAPTER IX

"Let Slip the Dogs of War!"

WHEN SCHOOLS were established to train dogs of various breeds, and dogs of no discernible breeds, for work in the World War, the project was looked on at first as a fantastic novelty. Even after the stigma, "fantastic," had been disproved by the glorious exploits of these hero dogs, their use still was deemed a novelty.

It was nothing of the kind. Dogs were organized for use in human warfare several thousand years ago. Perhaps long before that.

In the eternal petty wars among the Ionian Islanders, the Colophonian army was reinforced by a regiment of trained fighting dogs—enormous brutes with armored collars and breastplates. They formed the front rank of every mass attack and defense.

Their ravening jaws, and the long sharp spikes of their collars and breastplates, wrought nasty damage upon the foemen against whose lines they hurled themselves. They tangled and disrupted the enemy front, and thus they gave the men of their own army a fine chance to break through their opponents' disorganized vanguard.

These war dogs of Colophon had a reputation for advancing, all the time, till they were hewn to pieces;

"LET SLIP THE DOGS OF WAR!"

and never once of giving ground before the fiercest onslaught. They were a mighty auxiliary in the Ionian forces.

Besides their front-rank exploits, they were invaluable in covering the retreat in a lost battle. They fought savage "rearguard actions" at such times, keeping the pursuers busy with them till the last dog was cut down.

When the Athenians were at war with Corinth, fifty war dogs were kenneled in a row along the shore of the Gulf. Kenneled, but not chained. They were left loose, and sternly taught to stay where they were.

One evening, the Athenian fleet launched a surprise attack on Corinth; sending a flotilla of muffled-oar barges full of armed men ashore from the galleys. So dark was the night and so swiftly and silently the assault was carried out that the invaders landed and began to form their ranks for a raid on the city beyond, without a single human sentry hearing or seeing them.

But the fifty war dogs saw and heard—and scented. Forth from their kennels they raged. In a snarling and snapping throng they went for the newly landed raiders. The Athenians slew them right and left, as the fearless dogs swirled biting and tearing among them.

Forty-nine of the fifty canine warriors were slain. The fiftieth—a beast named Sotér—had more intelligence or less battle lust than his comrades. For, instead of throwing his life away in a futile effort to drive the Athenians back into the sea, he disobeyed the orders his trainers had given him "to stay where he was."

Away to the city he ran, with all speed. There he woke the night—and the garrison—with his thunder of barking and by tugging at the tunic of one officer after the other.

As a result, the garrison rushed to arms in time to repel the raid and to save the city from capture.

The Corinthians were duly grateful to Sotér for giving the warning. They built a column to the memory of the forty-nine dogs that had died in defense of the seacoast. At the top of the list was Sotér's name, with the added inscription, *"Sotér, Preserver of Corinth."*

As "Sotér" is the Greek word for "Preserver" or for "Saviour," a ponderous pun was intended. (Which passed for a witticism in those days.)

So much for a war dog which got an extra line on his epitaph because he had the wit to fight and run away rather than to die gallantly and stupidly and fruitlessly in defense of his country. He *saved* his country instead of dying for it. I think he must have had a strain of collie in his mixed ancestry.

I could go on for pages, citing the verified deeds of valor performed by canine heroes of old. But there is no need.

All I wanted was to show you that organized war dogs lived—and died—fighting most valiantly in defense of the fatherlands of their trainers more than twenty centuries before a crazed student shot an Austrian Grand Duke at Sarajevo in the summer of 1914 and thus lighted the unextinguished international spark which was to set the whole world ablaze.

If you do not believe war dogs were in general use before 1914—well, how about this line from *Julius*

"LET SLIP THE DOGS OF WAR!"

Caesar, written by one W. Shakespeare who died in 1616 A.D.?

"Cry 'Havoc!' And let slip the dogs of war!"

Shakespeare could not well have devised that phrase, "the dogs of war," before 1616, if war dogs were not known until the beginning of the World War in 1914, could he?

Now let us get down to more interesting and more concrete incidents.

(I am not talking about pampered regimental mascots, but about genuine dogs of war and of dogs which performed verified wartime exploits.)

After the World War's outset, the French trainers divided their service dogs roughly into two classes: "estafettes" and "liaison" dogs.

The estafettes had much the easier and safer time of it, although death found all too many of them. Their chief duty was to carry messages to certain specified points.

The liaison dogs not only had to carry such messages but must then return, with or without an answer from the recipient, to the point of starting. Double duty, double danger, and need for double intelligence and pluck.

One of the very foremost of the war's liaison dogs was a fearless mongrel nicknamed "Satan." From the time he was shipped from his training school to the front, he won praise for gallant and brilliant work under fire.

But it was at the bloody siege of Verdun that he gained immortal fame.

(At one sector around Verdun, by the way, seventeen human couriers were shot down in quick succession while they were carrying dispatches. And a single liaison dog ran with messages over the same deadly bit of territory seven times before he was killed.)

A village close to Verdun sprang into renown overnight because an unexpected twist in the battle game made it a key to several other important positions. The village was occupied by only a few hundred French soldiers at the time. Their commandant had orders to hold it at any cost until reinforcements should be sent forward to relieve him.

Then a large German force worked its way around the village and got behind it, enveloping the French position and cutting off its defenders from retreat and from communication with headquarters. For days the enemy hammered the village from all sides. For days the French fought off the attack.

The garrison's small numbers were cut to skeleton size. So were their food and ammunition. It became only a matter of a short time before they must fall easy prey to their besiegers. And no word of their terrible plight could be sent through to their own lines.

At last the Germans were able to bring up batteries to a near-by hill to the left of the village and to plant them there. This position commanded the whole place. A whirlwind of shells was vomited down upon the crumbling huddle of houses.

Unless those batteries could be silenced, the village and the garrison must be annihilated within a few hours.

"LET SLIP THE DOGS OF WAR!"

If word could be smuggled through to the French line, telling of the surprise move and giving the precise position of the German batteries, the long-range French guns could be trained accurately on the hill. And the Boche batteries could be silenced and smashed to flinders.

But how could such an SOS dispatch be taken through the network of steel and fire that girt the village? What messenger stood a Chinaman's chance of getting past the swarms of German snipers and the avalanche of shellfire?

Telephone and telegraph had been put out of commission. The last carrier pigeon had been shot down by snipers. No trained human scout could wriggle his way over half of the death-swept area. There were no war dogs in the place.

The commandant remembered the orders from headquarters to hold the village at all costs until reinforcements could come up. He would not surrender. In the face of absolutely certain destruction he and his men fought on.

Just then a sentinel reported that some impossibly queer creature was coming toward the village from the direction of the far-off French lines: an apparition with the body and legs of a shaggy dog but with a goggled and cone-shaped head and with a pair of clumsy wings flopping from his shoulder blades.

Field glasses were turned on the incredible beast. And the mystery of his goblin aspect was cleared up at a glance.

The newcomer was the hero war dog, Satan.

On his head was the gas mask that so many of his

four-footed fellows had been taught with much pain and difficulty to wear and which always caused them acute discomfort. Over his shoulders, by a harness, two baskets were swinging: baskets used for transporting carrier pigeons.

Satan was loping toward the village with the queer zig-zag gait his trainers had taught him to use when he was traveling under fire: a gait which rendered him a most difficult target for the average sharpshooting sniper.

How he had come, alive, thus near the village, adroitly skirting shell craters as he ran, was a mystery. He had been seen from all along the German line. Shells and shrapnel were trained on him. Sharpshooters peppered away zealously at him. For he was bringing to the beleaguered garrison a barely possible means of communicating with their own main body.

It was all-essential that he should be stopped before he and his cargo of carrier pigeons could reach their destination. Seldom has any one creature been the target for such a wholesale expert bombardment. Thousands of dollars' worth of costly German ammunition was expended that day on a mongrel dog whose peacetime cash value had not exceeded seventy-five cents.

While the garrison watched, spellbound, Satan leaped in air, then pitched headforemost to the ground. A sniper's high-power bullet had drilled him at last.

The commandant groaned aloud at this loss of his one last hope. Then a cry of amazement broke from the throats of the whole decimated garrison.

Slowly the dog was lurching to his feet. He was be-

WITH A GOGGLED AND CONE-SHAPED HEAD AND A PAIR OF WINGS FLOPPING FROM HIS SHOULDER BLADES

"LET SLIP THE DOGS OF WAR!"

wildered and he seemed uncertain what to do next or which way to go. Again the hail of enemy bullets concentrated upon him.

But almost instantly Satan got his wits and his bearings again. At a sweeping gallop—still running in that bafflingly elusive way—he set forth afresh for the trenches of the village. His line of advance was accompanied by a tornado of German fire.

Then a second bullet found him. Again he tumbled to the shell-pocked earth. But, as before, he was up and on his journey. Unswervingly he kept on. Though now he must travel on three legs. For his right foreleg was splintered.

No longer could he travel so fast, or use the bullet-dodging gait his trainers had taught him. Yet it did not occur to his great white soul to call it a day and to collapse under his two wounds and under the mortal agony that racked him. At the best speed he could master, he limped on to the trenches.

There many hands seized him and drew him down out of the line of firing. He was carried lovingly to the commandant. The two fluttering and badly jostled carrier pigeons—there had been one of them in each basket—were put into coops where they could quiet down.

In a brass tube fastened to Satan's collar was a message from the main line. It told the commandant that the garrison would be relieved on the following day, and that he must hold out, at all hazards, until then.

Relief would be sent next day!

Next day? By that time—long before that time—there would be no garrison left to rescue, no position left to hold. The Germans would be in undisputed control of the village, and far too strongly entrenched for any chance of dislodging them.

The keystone of that whole sector's French defense would be shattered. The rallying cry: *"They shall not pass!"* would have become a mouthful of empty words.

With only a ragged remnant of men left alive—with the ammunition all but gone—with the Germans on the hill to the left—there would be no "tomorrow" for the commandant and his soldiers. It was at most a matter of hours, just then. Not of days or of a single day. Naturally, headquarters did not know the Germans had captured the hill. And there was only one faint chance of letting headquarters learn of it.

The commandant wrote a note, in duplicate, telling of the new phase of the village's siege and describing accurately the position of the German hill batteries. A copy of this note was fastened to each of the two carrier pigeons.

The birds were tossed aloft. Once or twice they circled high in air, to get their bearings. Then they set off, winging for the main line.

Naturally the German snipers had known what was in those two baskets that flapped from Satan's shoulder blades. Naturally they knew the birds would be sent back immediately with tidings of the garrison's awful need. They were ready, when the two pigeons flew up from the trenches.

The best sharpshooters in the corps opened fire on them.

It was pretty shooting, considering the range, and the smallness and swiftness of the targets. And there were plenty of marksmen seeking to bring down the birds.

Before the pigeons had flown a hundred meters, one of them toppled earthward, tumbling over and over in the air.

By a miracle the second bird was not hit. He winged his way out of range and out of sight, flying homeward to his coop inside the French lines.

An hour afterward, there was an earth-shaking multiple roar from the French long-range guns. The hill batteries were pounded to fragments. The German bombardment was dead. The village garrison was able to hold out till reinforcements came up.

All because one hairy mongrel had refused to die while his errand was still uncompleted; and because he was too loyal or too stupid (do the two words mean sometimes the same thing?) to quit.

There would be plenty of time to treat his tortured body to the luxury of death after his day's work should be done. And there was.

About the time when Satan was saving the key village and possibly shaping the whole history of the Verdun campaign and thus the fortunes of France and of the Allies, I and some other Americans were trying strenuously to combat an anti-dog crusade here in the United States; a crusade which clamored for the cutting down of the canine population.

This on the grounds that all dogs were useless, mere parasites, that they served no worth-while purpose anywhere, and that they gobbled food whose cost would "help win the war."

At that very hour, Satan and countless others of his profession were saving human lives in battle after battle; and were guiding Red Cross workers to grievously wounded men who had been left undiscovered on the field.

Yet in England and in France, when the war started, there was the same gross ignorance as to the martial work which dogs could perform. The Germans were wiser in such matters. For years, they had been training corps of intelligent dogs for use in the inevitable war which was ever nearer at hand.

When at last war was declared, there were several thousand intensively trained dogs attached to the German armies. The French had only a half handful of war dogs. The British, apparently, had none. So in France and in Great Britain there was perforce a scurry to establish training kennels and to find efficient trainers.

It was here that Lieutenant-Colonel Richardson of the British army proved himself invaluable. Long before then he had visited Germany and had seen the hordes of skilled war dogs and had noted how rigorously they were educated.

He knew military Germany did nothing without definite practical object. If a fortune was spent there to train dogs for war, then Germany must have a very solid reason for believing in war dogs' value. So Colonel Richardson tried to interest England and France and Belgium in a similar experiment.

Apparently, nobody was interested. For a time he had to content himself with educating his own dogs for possible martial use. In his monumental book, *Watch Dogs,* he tells of these prewar experiences:

"I paid several visits to their [the Germans'] training establishments. But I quickly saw we had the advantage in this country: by the possession of a better choice of dogs for the work. Also I questioned whether the immensely detailed system of training the keepers of the dogs, and also the dogs themselves, was to any useful purpose.

"It seemed to me that, as in other forms of German organization, not enough attention was paid to the psychology of the subject; and too much to the letter of mechanical construction.

"I knew that, in the event of dogs being employed at all in war, large supplies of them, and quickly trained, would be needed. Therefore, a quicker system of instruction was required. At all events in our country [England] where no preparations were being made in peacetime, for this branch.

"When the thunderbolt of war fell in this country ... I saw at once that a properly organized system of sentinel-and-guard dogs, all over the country, would be of enormous service.... I very urgently represented this, and offered to present my whole kennel of trained dogs to the army, that experiments might immediately be made.

"My ideas, however, were not in any way understood at the time. And I could make no headway."

Failing to rouse his own nation's war office to the tremendous need of war dogs, Colonel Richardson carried his efforts across the Channel. Here, for a time, he had scant success. Yet little by little the various governments, including his own, began to understand.

Then there was a scramble for the establishing of war-dog colleges everywhere; not only for educating the dogs themselves, but the soldiers who were to act as their trainers. Colonel Richardson was sent for, belatedly, by the British War Office, and he was appointed "Commandant of the British War-Dog School." He threw himself heart and soul into his new work; backed by intimate knowledge of dogs and a lifelong study of their natures.

As fast as a batch of dogs were trained, they and their trainers were shipped to the front. Back to the colonel drifted such reports as these:

"From O.C., 56th Brigade, Royal Field Artillery: . . . Both dogs reached headquarters, traveling . . . 4,000 yards over ground they had never seen before, and over an exceptionally difficult terrain. The dog dispatched at 12.45 P.M. reached his destination under the hour, bringing an important message; and this was the first message which was received, all visual communication having failed."

Also:

"On the attack of Vimy Ridge, dogs were employed with an artillery observation post. All the telephones were broken. Visual signaling was impossible. The dogs were the first to bring news through."

And:

"Jim, by his excellent services and consistency, has justly earned the C. O.'s commendation. While in the recent offensive in Belgium, Jim carried important dispatches in wonderfully quick time. It is certain no one else could have delivered such dispatches under such terrific and heavy shellfire without meeting bodily harm. On another occasion . . . Jim was instrumental in first giving the warning of gas; due no doubt to his highly sensitive nose."

Richardson had ideas of his own as to the education of war-school dogs. First and foremost, he forbade cruelty of any kind. If he found a trainer or an attendant who was unkind to one of the dogs, the man was fired from his job. He avoided all forms of coercion—all the time-dishonored methods of professional trick-dog trainers and of too many trainers of hunting dogs and collies.

The whip and the boot toe had no part in the teaching of these undergraduate war dogs in Richardson's school and in the schools he supervised. He made his whole appeal to the dog's interest in its work, in its pride in mastering the practical things that were taught to it, to its courage and to its adaptability and to its loyalty; in short, a general appeal to that mystic loyalty which binds dog to man and which makes him so eager to serve and obey his human god.

When any dog, after reasonable time, did not respond to such a line of teaching, that dog was dropped from the school. The training was to be a life-and-death matter to innumerable imperiled soldiers later on. And a stupid or cowardly or disobedient dog would be of no use at the front.

So much for the World War dogs and for the mass-production methods for turning them from friendly household pets to vigilant and wise and heroic canine soldiers. Their only pay was a scant amount of unpalatable food. Their lives were in danger, day and night. There was no "blighty" for them to rest their ripped nerves. There were no medals, no cheers, for their deeds of valor. No lure of an aureate bonus.

With their entrails torn out by a shell or with their backs broken by a bullet, they lay and writhed away their gallant lives unheeded; and their stanch bodies had no graves. Diseases of the skin and of the intestines—insufficient and bad food—overexertion and unslaked thirst—these were but a few of the pretty casualties that destroyed them by the hundred.

They saved a myriad lives. They helped turn the fortunes of the war. And they got nothing out of the whole sorry grind, except eventual death. Truly, "a dog's life!"

And don't forget, please, that noble crusade in America, waged at the same time, to abolish dogs as food-wasting parasites!

Now let's get to less well-organized war-dogs' experiences in earlier and less well-organized conflicts. One or two of these latter experiences are rather interesting, I think.

Napoleon wrote during his exile years concerning an incident of the Italian campaign. He said he had made an inspection of a battlefield at the close of one of the summer's bloodiest conflicts. A dog sprang out at him from beside a dead soldier, then ran back and licked the slain man's hand, moaning grievously. Again and again the beast tried to make Bonaparte do something to revive the corpse.

The petty incident stayed in Napoleon's memory,

through all the triumph years that followed so fast and so thick upon it. During his final days of exile, the fallen emperor wrote the story of the dead man's guardian dog; then continued:

"Perhaps it was the spirit of the time and the place that affected me. But I assure you no occurrence of any of my other battlefields impressed me so keenly. I halted on my tour to gaze on the spectacle, and to reflect on its meaning.

"This soldier, I realized, must have had friends at home and in his regiment; yet he lay there deserted by all except his dog. . . . I had looked on, unmoved, at battles which decided the future of nations. Tearless, I had given orders which brought death to thousands.

"Yet, here I was stirred, profoundly stirred, stirred to tears. And by what? By the grief of one dog. I am certain that at that instant I felt more ready than at any other time to show mercy toward a suppliant foeman. I could understand just then the tinge of mercy which led Achilles to yield the corpse of his enemy, Hector, to the weeping Priam."

Almost a half century after Napoleon's day another soldier's little dog won international fame through the stories written of his adventures. He was a mongrel, known as Hans. As a shivering puppy he crept into the officers' mess at the Vienna cavalry barracks.

An officer shouted to one of the military stewards to kick the cur down the steps and into the street. Before the command could be obeyed, a captain stepped between Hans and the steward. The captain was Karl

Weiss, a solitary man who had few friends and no intimates.

Weiss picked up the shivering and half-starved puppy and carried it to his own quarters. Why he did such a thing—why he kept Hans and made a lifelong chum of him—nobody knew. It was a theme for much mirth in the barracks.

Several of the officers of the crack regiment owned dogs which paced solemnly at their heels. But all these animals were of royally high pedigree, and they had cost their owners a stupendous price. It was a matter of pride and of eternal rivalry to be able to boast of owning the most expensive blueblooded thoroughbred in the barracks.

Yet here was Captain Weiss annexing a homely little mutt, of no breed, and of all breeds mixed together. It was incredible. Almost a slur on the regiment.

Weiss was a dead shot, and he was peerless with a saber. His savage courage and marvelous prowess had been proven more than once on the dueling field. Solitary and reticent as he was, yet decidedly he was not a man to make fun of. So the other officers kept their jokes about Hans from reaching the ears of the mongrel's new owner. Meanwhile, man and dog had become wholeheartedly devoted to each other.

When Weiss's regiment was ordered to the front, the next summer, Hans was taken along. During a battle, early in the campaign, the dog was tied to his master's tent, far to the rear. At the end of the day, Captain Weiss was reported missing. Search of the battlefield was made in vain. Then the captain's military servant had an idea.

He galloped back to Weiss's tent, untied Hans, and rode to the field again, carrying the dog across his saddlebow. He set Hans on the ground there, saying to him:

"Master! Find *Master!*"

Off ran the dog, nose to earth. He quartered the field, like a pointer or a setter. Long and fast he ran. Then through the twilight the searchers heard his shrill yelping.

They hurried on. And they came at last to a heap of dead men. Hans was scratching furiously at the topmost bodies, trying to dislodge them. All the time he kept up that shrill volley of yelps.

At the bottom of the pile of dead, Captain Karl Weiss was found lying, unconscious and seemingly lifeless. He was carried to the field hospital, Hans trailing behind him and taking an undisputed place of his own at the bottom of the wounded man's cot.

There the dog stayed until his master was nursed back to life and to health.

The story spread all over Austria and to other lands. In a trice the ugly little crossbreed had ceased to be a mutt and blossomed into a hero. Thereafter, the regimental officers made no more slurring jests about Weiss's dog; even among themselves.

For another seven years Hans and his master lived happily together in camp and in barracks and at home. The dog was no more interested in the general praise that was showered on him than he had been in the earlier grins of contempt. He was a one-man dog. And Captain Karl Weiss was the one man.

Then came another war. Again Weiss was reported

missing after a battle. And again Hans was called upon to find him. For the second time the dog led the searchers to the wounded man. But this time the surgeons pronounced Weiss's wounds to be fatal.

They told him he had but a few days to live. By sheer will power, Weiss fought back death for a time. He had himself transported to his home in Vienna; while Hans crouched on his breast throughout the tedious journey. At his home the dying captain was put to bed. He sent instantly for his lawyer and had a will drawn up.

In this testament he directed that all his small fortune be left to his only relative, a middle-aged cousin, on condition that she give Hans a good home for the rest of the dog's existence and that she supply him with every possible comfort. He appointed trustworthy executors to see she carried out the terms of the will.

Weiss had kept himself alive until he could provide for his loved dog's future. Now there was nothing to struggle for. He snapped his fingers. Hans leaped onto the bed, at the long-familiar signal. Weiss's hand passed caressingly over his mongrel's stiff hair.

Then the hand fell limply to the counterpane. Hans made the room re-echo with a screaming death howl for the man whose life had just ended.

The provisions of the captain's will were not followed out. There was no need. For the little dog starved himself to death during the following few days.

Nobody appears to know where Mafeking came from, or in what official capacity he first was inducted into war work. Probably he started his martial career as a killer of the rats that infested his regiment's barracks.

He sprang into fame during the Boer War in South Africa toward the end of the last century; at the historic siege of Mafeking.

What his original name may have been I never heard. But presently the British soldiers began to call him "Mafeking," after the besieged town wherein he and they were cooped so long. And the name stuck. By it the dog became known to all the world during the next year or so.

The small town of Mafeking was a pivotal point at that period of the Boer War. It stood at a river edge in the midst of open country, nearly a mile above sea level.

When a Boer army besieged the place, it was defended by a none-too-large British force under command of Colonel Baden-Powell. Against fearful odds they held Mafeking stubbornly against the attacks of the Boers for two hundred and seventeen days; before a British relief column could fight its way through to them and scatter their assailants.

It was in that long-drawn-out inferno of noise and hunger and sudden death that the scrubby little Irish terrier, "Mafeking," strutted to fame.

He was a born fighter. And he made the British cause his own. He was not content with his allotted jobs of ratcatcher and camp watchdog and scavenger. He wanted action. And he got it. In big doses.

His first recorded venture of the kind was when the front-line defenses of the beleaguered British were under a terrific bombardment one morning from the Staats Artillery gunners.

Scorning the shelter of the bombproofs, young Mafeking strutted forth toward the outer defense line and beyond it. Kindly hands reached up to grab him and drag him back. But the terrier had no trouble at all in ducking them. On he went, straight into the face of the enemy's guns.

All honor to the gunners in those Staats Artillery batteries! Yes, and to the unerringly accurate Boer sharpshooters massed in support of them!

Here was an auburn Irish dog swaggering truculently toward them, after his scramble over the last protective parapet; and out into the open line of fire.

Did they take potshots at him? Did they blow him into cat's meat with a shell? They did nothing of the kind. They were sportsmen, those Boers. Believe it or not, but the war's history gives solemn record that every battery's every gun fell silent. Not a sniper touched finger to trigger.

In brief, for the first and presumably for the last time in the world's blood-smeared annals of warfare, a battle stopped short; lest one small dog be hurt. Yes, it sounds like a tall story. But it is true. Once more, all honor to the Boers and to their big-hearted sportsmanship!

There the bombardment halted, figuratively in midair, while Mafeking strolled self-importantly, with tulip ears and impudent tail stump cocked, along the open space between the two lines. No onlooker could doubt that he knew in some occult canine way the wholesale sensation he was creating.

"LET SLIP THE DOGS OF WAR!"

At last, he tired of his stroll in the glaring heat of the sun. He consented to listen to the imperative shouts of the British behind bombproof and parapet, commanding him with lurid blasphemies to come back to safety. He loafed to the spot whence he had begun his pleasant morning ramble.

There he was yanked behind the parapet, and was tied up to keep him from another such outing. This, while the Boer batteries burst forth into a new blast of death.

I'll say that is a mighty good little story of a mighty good little dog. And I believe you will agree with me. Word of it, in course of time, traveled around the world. But it was not the end of Mafeking's war adventures.

A very few days after his excursion into the jaws of death, Mafeking was walking across a street, far back in the town, intent on affairs of his own. There was a rattle high above, as of rails piled loosely on a fast-moving truck over a bumpy road. A Boer shell burst on the roadway directly in front of him.

A fragment of metal plowed its way into Mafeking's rufous body—the body the Boers had saved from harm by stopping their own bombardment. The limply unconscious terrier was picked up with all tenderness and care and carried to the nearest hospital ward.

There was plenty of work for the British surgeons in those days, tending the sick and wounded men in their charge. Yet the most skillful of them found time to toil over the injured Irish terrier as sedulously as if the victim had been Colonel Baden-Powell himself.

As a result, Mafeking got well.

The first day he was allowed to go out alone he made a beeline for the open ground beyond the defenses and into close range of the Boer guns. Doglike, he sought to give an encore of his former spectacular stunt.

To his snarling indignation, a British soldier collared him and scooped him up and tied him to a post in a bombproof, before he could reach his objective. After that, strict watch was kept over him, and he found no further chance to silence the Staats Artillery batteries.

So he began doing psychic things. One night, he darted from one end of a dormitory building to the other, biting the sleeping soldiers and yanking the blankets off them. All this time he was barking and screeching at the top of his lungs.

The whole dormitory was aroused. Next, Mafeking galloped out of the building and then back again, mutely urging the sleepy soldiers to leave the place. The men had an uncanny faith in his intuition. Grumbling, they followed him out into the barracks square.

A few seconds afterward a Boer shell struck the dormitory building and smashed it to pieces.

From that time onward, the terrier was regarded by the men as something supernatural.

(I can't explain why he knew the shell was coming. Any more than I can explain why my own queer little blind collie, Sunnybank Fair Ellen, would wheel about and bark wildly a full second before a heavy thunderclap sounded. Dogs have certain senses not given to us humans—senses which enable them at times to foreknow happenings that are about to take place.

I don't think there is anything supernatural about

it. I believe it is wholly explainable, if only we could hit on the secret. To a dog it must seem like the most impossible feat of witchcraft when a man presses a button in the wall and floods a pitch dark room with dazzling white light. That is, if the dog takes the trouble to notice the miracle at all. Which I don't believe he does.)

Even yet, Mafeking's warlike adventures were not at an end. He was a natural-born Receptacle for Trouble.

The shell which crumpled the dormitory building was the first shot of a heavy bombardment of the town. Mafeking was trotting complacently across the Market Square, soon after his psychic saving of the sleepers, when another shell fragment laid him out.

This time he was slower in getting well, in spite of all the eager surgical care lavished upon him. For food was scarce. He could get nothing nourishing to eat during his convalescence.

The town's defenders were all but starving. Their supply of provisions had run perilously low. Now, for the most part, the garrison's rations consisted of grain husks and oats, mixed with a sweetish decoction of glycerine and drenched with a weak gravy made from the stewed bones and skins of eaten horses. On such a lean diet a wounded little Irish terrier does not pick up much strength.

But the dog got well. He did more. He went through the rest of the severe campaign—this time without a scratch—and after the war he was taken back to England to finish his life in drowsy peace.

Luck to his trouble-hunting soul; in whatever part

of the universe it may chance to be strutting cockily today!

We spoke a moment or so ago of the psychic powers which told Mafeking when the dormitory building was about to be hit by a shell. Here is another such incident of a war dog's odd premonition:

"William the Silent"—Prince of Orange—was struggling, in the 1570's, to free the Netherlands from Spanish misrule. On William's life alone hung the venture's slim chances of success. The Bloody Duke of Alva headed the Spanish army. And that army outnumbered by far the Prince of Orange's puny forces.

During the campaign, William's best friend and his official night guard was his toy spaniel. A human sentry might sleep on duty or he might be bought over by the enemy. The spaniel could neither be bribed nor be caught napping.

One night William was visiting an outpost of his scattered and half-equipped Dutch army. Word of his presence was carried to the Spaniards by a spy. A surprise attack was organized hastily—an attack whose sole objective was the capture or the killing of William.

With the prince out of the way, the rebellious Netherlanders would be easy prey to their conquerors. The revolution would be stamped out, with much speed and with much more slaughter. From the spy the raiders learned the exact position of the tent wherein the prince was to sleep, that night, on his tour of the outposts.

The attack was made in due form and with much zest

"LET SLIP THE DOGS OF WAR!"

and precision. It was a complete success—until it happened to collide with a tiny obstacle with four legs and silky fur and an engraved silver collar.

Thanks to the negligence or the bribing of the sentinels, the onrushing Spanish cavalry were in the very heart of the Netherlands camp before their presence was suspected. To the tent of the Prince of Orange galloped the riders.

Five minutes earlier, a small spaniel had jumped up on the slumbering prince's shoulder and had clawed diligently at his cheeks and gnawed still more diligently at his royal nose. There was no shaking him off.

William knew dogs too well to disregard the frantic warning. He jumped into a few clothes, shouted for his escort and stuck the barking dog into the pocket of his coat, and vaulted to the back of the horse which always was kept waiting and saddled outside his tent.

Off galloped William, through the night; a bare dozen jumps ahead of the Spanish assassins who rushed into his newly emptied tent.

The cause of the Netherlanders was saved. All because of a toy war dog.

Motley, the historian, tells us William ever afterward kept a spaniel of the same vigilant strain to guard his sleep. Portraits and statues of the prince nearly all include a toy spaniel standing or lying vigilantly at his royal master's side.

By the way—this has nothing to do with our story—I used to think of William the Silent as a glumly taciturn old cuss; poor company at best; because of his refusal or inability to converse. Then I read more about him, and I understood. Ordinarily, he was not silent at all. He used to talk much and at great length.

But when, as a page, he was on duty for a time at the French court, he listened to the discussion of plans to subjugate his country and to wipe out his religious denomination. To all these projects he hearkened without a word; merely storing them up for future use.

Afterward, when he was able to do something to block the plots against his fatherland and his religion, he profited by what he had heard when he had stood wordless and seemingly dull and inattentive behind the chair of the French king. Because of his early discretion and of his ability to keep his mouth shut at the right time, he was nicknamed "William the Silent."

As I just told you, this morsel of vicarious information has nothing whatever to do with your book and mine. But it is mildly interesting, isn't it?

And now shall we pass on to the tale of one more war dog and of his dramatic experiences?

His name was "Thoutou." He was attached to the Third French Zouave Regiment in the expedition against the Beni-Raten tribes in the Kabylia country of Africa.

Thoutou's official job was to rout out enemy snipers from the thickets around the Zouave camp and to make nightly patrols of the line of French sentries.

In his puppyhood he had been caught and tortured by a band of Arabs. Since that time he could smell an Arab, from any distance. And the scent always in-

"LET SLIP THE DOGS OF WAR!" 253

furiated him. This trait added vastly to his value as a sentinel dog.

Of a hot day, a man dressed in the uniform and wearing the insignia of the First Zouaves rode into the bivouac of the Third. He was on dispatch duty, he said; and he stopped to enjoy the hospitality of his fellows at the midday meal. They made him welcome. His white teeth flashed smilingly from his dark face—a face as dark as any Arab's—while he acknowledged their welcoming greetings.

In the midst of the luncheon on the sands, and while the merry guest was plying his Zouave hosts with anecdotes and with guileless questions, Thoutou trotted up to the table from a round of the dense thickets which encircled the camp.

The big dog went straight toward the guest. Then he halted and sniffed the air. Then he growled murderously and threw himself at the stranger's throat. He was pried away. But his fury had aroused suspicion. For he made friends always with any Zouave.

The guest was questioned more closely as to his regiment and his destination. Under threat of the struggling Thoutou's thunderous growls, his replies waxed incoherent, vague, self-contradictory. He was led to the commandant. There, investigation showed him to be a clever Arab spy, in Zouave uniform.

The spy's perfect disguise and his superficial knowledge of the corps' routine had deceived his entertainers. They had babbled freely to him. But the elusive Arab reek of his body had told Thoutou who and what he was.

Not much later, the Third Zouaves stormed the

Arab position at Palestro. The natives had drawn up their artillery on the far side of a water-filled ditch. The caissons still had the horses attached to them, in case of need for sudden retreat.

As the Zouaves advanced and as the Arab artillery beyond the ditch opened fire, Thoutou deserted his place at the rear of the French line. Disregarding orders, he sprang, barking gaily, into the wide ditch. He proceeded to swim across, under a futile fire from Arab muskets.

The Zouaves, inspired by his example, and wishing to save him from death, leaped into the bullet-sprayed water and swam to the far side, in his wake. This, without waiting as usual for orders from their officers. Carrying their rifles high above their heads with one hand, they made the passage.

As soon as his feet found bottom, on the opposite side of the ditch, Thoutou scrambled up the steep bank; before the Arabs could spear him or shoot him.

The native defenders were wheeling their caisson horses, to bring their cannon into play upon the swimming Zouaves. Thoutou seemed to know what the maneuver meant. He dashed among the milling horses, slashing their noses, nipping their hocks, filling them with panic terror which made them plunge and veer and buck and bolt.

The Arabs' line of cannon was a tangle of hopeless confusion. The guns' muzzles were pointing everywhere and anywhere and nowhere; while the drivers sought to regain control over their scared and plunging horses and while Thoutou's wild assaults made such realignment impossible.

The swimming Zouaves gained the bank, almost unchecked. They hurled themselves into the scrimmage of bolting and squealing cannon horses and confused cannoneers. The battle was won with ridiculous ease.

Thanks to a big dog, that did not like the smell of Arabs and that had a genius for producing chaos out of military order.

Then there were campaigns for Thoutou in Morocco and in Mexico and elsewhere—campaigns wherein he conducted himself right brilliantly and in one of which the latter half of his tail was carried away by a dumdum bullet.

When at last his Third Zouaves were sent home and garrisoned in France, in the late 1860's, Thoutou was demobilized. He was billeted for life at the house of a human comrade near Versailles. There, to the day of his death, he was a peerless hero to the children and the veterans of the neighborhood.

Apart from his severed tail, Thoutou had come through fourteen campaigns with the Zouaves without a serious injury. This, though his official record with the French War Office cited "two wounds and three contusions."

The hurts were not serious, any of them—except the halving of the tail of which he was so justly proud—and they were not regarded by the ancient canine hero at all as serious handicaps to an old age of comfort and of well-earned repose.

So much for the careers of a mere smattering of war dogs, out of many thousand which merit as much space and as much praise. Throughout the ages the dog has been used in one capacity or another in warfare.

So, ever and with ever-increasing efficiency, he will continue to be used.

He, who asks nothing better than to guard his master and his master's peaceful home, will be trained better and better into his role in the Iron Game of Universal Slaughter. He won't want to do such direful work. But he will be taught to by those he trusts. And, being only a dog, he will obey.

For his life-risking—almost invariably for his life-losing—heroism, he will receive no pay, no glory. To him, it ever must be all a part of the day's work:

> *Not his is the planning and plotting,*
> *And naught can he profit thereby.*
> *But his is the dying and rotting.*
> *The poor little guy!*

In which condition (though without the hope of wartime pay and of a plump bonus) he will share the fate—as for so many centuries he has shared it—of the average doughboy.

God help him!

CHAPTER X

Some Freak Dogs

I DON'T KNOW why some dogs have freak minds which lead them to do freak deeds and to behave at variance with all recognized canine conduct.

But then I don't know why George Francis Train used to go about the New York streets in winter, forty years ago, bareheaded and clad in white. Nor why in that same primly correct era of primly correct costumes, Dr Mary Walker cajoled Congress into passing a bill permitting her to wear men's trousers and a high hat.

Dogs have no monopoly on freakdom. But their eccentricities are less annoying and more amusing than those of freak humans. For instance:

In my own mental picture gallery of queer dogs, Bose stands out pre-eminent. He was a cross between a collie and an Irish setter; the collie strain predominating in looks and in mind. He was one of the wisest dogs I have known, and yet he was by all odds the craziest. He appeared to take elfin delight in reversing certain established processes of reasoning.

Bose belonged to one of my sisters. He spent the bulk of his time at Sunnybank. At night he slept on the floor of my room.

When one of the maids rapped at my door to wake

me in the morning, and if I did not answer, Bose jumped lightly onto the bed and proceeded to shake me by the shoulder until I opened my eyes. Then he went back to his rug on the floor.

I might continue to lie in bed for another hour or more. That was no affair of Bose's. He had shaken me awake. His duty went no further. Whether or not I might choose to get up, was my own affair. Not Bose's. His job was performed. Never did he try to wake me a second time, the same morning.

He constituted himself the tireless and continuous guard of my sister's eldest son, Fritz, a child of eight. Bose adored the boy and went everywhere with him.

But—let any grown person pretend to strike or to kick Fritz!

Perhaps you think you know the answer? The loyal guardian dog flew raveningly at the assailant's throat? Well, you are wrong. The loyal guardian dog did nothing of the kind.

The loyal guardian dog flew at the little boy, *not* at the aggressor; and proceeded to bite him sharply, two or three times.

Again and again, with Fritz's amused consent, I would ask some guest—some man whom Bose never before had seen—to stride truculently up to my nephew and to strike at him with one fist after the other, or to pretend to kick him.

Never once did Bose fail to nip growlingly the first part of his young master's body he could reach.

I can't explain this reverse English on all accepted watchdog procedure; unless perhaps on the theory that the fake blow or kick made Bose think Fritz had done something wrong which called for punishment; and that his own duty as guardian called upon him to inflict some part of that chastisement.

In the summer of 1899, I was reading, under a tree, in the orchard, at Sunnybank. The hay had been cut a day or so earlier. My three nephews were romping in it, about a hundred feet from me. Bose lay drowsing in the shade near them.

It occurred to Fritz that it would be an excellent idea for all three of them to go over to the dog and, at a signal, to sit down on his recumbent body; then to fill his snappingly protesting mouth with hay.

The plan was carried out with brilliant success. Bose struggled wildly. But he could not dislodge the triple weight. Into his threatening jaws much good hay was jammed by the boys. Then Fritz said:

"I wonder what Bose will do if we all three get up off him at the same time."

"I know perfectly well what he'll do," I made answer from under my distant tree. "He knows I'm the only one who had no part in teasing him. So, as fast as he can get to his feet, he'll come tearing over here and bite *me*."

Which he did.

Later the same afternoon, on the Sunnybank veranda, I was telling my father about it. Bose was snoozing at the foot of the porch. Apart from being a clergyman, my father was also an inspired dogman. He had much greater power over dogs than ever I have had. There was little canine lore he had not learned and practised. When I had told him the somewhat pointless tale, he said:

"It was your own fault. You romp too much with Bose. He has no respect for you. You'll have noticed the dog never does that kind of thing to *me*. I see to it that he always treats me with gentle deference."

Bose got up from his nap. He stretched himself lazily, fore and aft. He loafed up the porch steps to where we sat. Gravely he nipped my father's ankles, one after the other. Then he snatched the new soft hat from my father's head and carried it out on the lawn and rolled on it.

The next Christmas Eve, my brother-in-law (the three children's father) hit on a plan for enhancing his sons' faith in Santa Claus. The night was brilliantly moonlit. He was to put on a fur coat and cap and white whiskers, and was to hang a big stuffed sack over his shoulders.

Then, at a signal, we were to take the children to the bay window of the living room; to look out at the moonlit snow. As they were gazing, Santa Claus was to hurry past, along the drive, just below, on his way to the chimney.

If that glimpse did not make each and every one of the three youngsters believe fanatically in the existence of a real Saint Nick, nothing could.

The signal cough sounded. The children were herded to the bay window. A figure appeared, bounding merrily along the snow crust.

There was a multiple gasp of incredulous ecstasy from the three little boys. For, as natural as life, Santa Claus was crossing the patch of gleaming moonlight. Pack and whiskers and all.

Then came a second gasp from the boys. This time

of horrified consternation. For a new figure had flashed onto the shining Yuletide scene.

Around the house's corner and into full view galloped the besotted Bose, in hot pursuit. He launched himself with riotous zeal upon the fast-running Santa.

In practically a single gesture of the dog's swift jaws, the bulging pack was ripped from its shoulder moorings and was sent rolling in the snow; where immediately the white whiskers and the fur cap joined it.

All praise be to the impersonator of the Patron Saint of Christmas!

Instead of whanging the plot-marring dog's wicked head off, the despoiled Santa sat down in the snow, yelling helplessly with laughter. This, while Bose gamboled in noisy glee around him; tempting him to further Christ-tide merriment.

This, too, while we spectators hustled the three starkly staring children back from the window; and tried to explain to them that Santa and Bose were old friends, and that the seemingly horrific scene of sacrilege they had witnessed was just a yearly romp which both participants enjoyed ever so much and always looked forward to.

(Fritz, the eldest of the three boys—Bose's young master and lifelong idol—is now far-famed in the world of literature and in the world of men. He is known to you and to the rest of the reading public as Frederic F. Van de Water. Incidentally, he is, by far, my best-loved friend and boon companion.)

In those prehistoric days, peddlers roamed the North Jersey hinterland. One of them had a wooden leg.

He used to make recurrent visits to Sunnybank with his wares. As he stumped down the furlong of wooded twisting driveway from the highroad, Bose used to frolic forward and upward to meet him.

The dog would wag his tail in glad welcome to the visitor and pat at him with his white fore paws. Then, invariably, he would drop behind the peddler and bite him. Not lightly, as he nipped the rest of us, but with vehement intensity.

And *always* in the wooden leg.

It was not an act of treachery, but presumably an attempt to expose a fake.

In his last days, Bose tackled a crossbreed dog, half mastiff, half St Bernard. A dog of more than twice his size and weight and of much less than half his age. His battle wounds were deep; though we throttled the larger dog from him before the carnage was complete.

Bose was indignant with us for days, for intervening to save his life. Never did he recover wholly from the battle. He is buried near the lake edge; amid a long line of other grand Sunnybank dogs of the past eighty years.

There are only a few Sunnybank dogs that are not buried in that hidden old graveyard. The exceptions are Lad, who lies beneath his best-loved resting place close to the house, at the foot of a shade tree; Bruce and Bruce's daughter, Jean, who sleep side by side, as in life, a little farther up the slope; and the dogs which surround a woodland boulder called by many newspapers "Champions' Rock."

Those dogs are our shining champions, Sunnybank

Sigurd (the "Treve" of my book of that name), Sunnybank Sigurdson, Sunnybank Explorer and Sunnybank Thane. There, too, sleep our non-champion immortals, Gray Dawn, Wolf, Bobby and Fair Ellen. When Sandy shall die he is to lie there too. No more dogs after that.

At a little distance from the rock is a tiny grave—the grave of Tippy, the temperamental gray Persian cat—"the cat that thought she was a dog"—our little housemate for more than fifteen pleasant years.

So much for so much. Now let's turn our backs on necrology and return to the crack-wit army of freak dogs, shan't we?

Treve—our golden Champion Sunnybank Sigurd—is the next in line.

Treve spent his whole short life and all of his best endeavors in trying to be incurably mean and treacherous and hateful. Gallantly as he struggled toward that ignoble goal, he succeeded only in being one of the most obedient and most white-hearted and gentlest dogs I have owned.

But he was a freak.

Even as a puppy, he would search worriedly in the straw for a bone (which he did not want.) and would rummage every corner of his bed for it. When I would find the bone for him—it was in plain sight all the time—he would snarl at me and would bury it deep beneath the straw again; and renew his silly hunt for it. That was one of his favorite games.

Another pastime was his refusal to eat a single mouthful of his one big daily meal. Let his feeder turn his back for an instant; and the food was gone. But it had not vanished down Treve's furry throat. Carefully, it was hidden under the edges of his flaring feed dish or in a new-dug hole in the near-by earth.

To make him dine (in order to keep up his needed condition as a stud and show dog) we would summon our fiery little red-gold collie, Wolf, to the feast. Then and only then would Sigurd consent to eat; gulping down his dinner, mouthful by mouthful, and punctuating his meal by roaring insults at the boredly watching Wolf—Wolf who could have destroyed his own stocky weight in tigers, and who understood the game perfectly well.

At Treve's last dog show—at Huntington, Pa.—where he won the final victory points which made him a Champion of Record in the books of the American Kennel Club—we used the familiar cry of "Wolf! I'll give your dinner to *Wolf!*" to stir him from crestfallen hot-weather apathy to a glint of the flaming excitement which was his when Wolf was called to steal his dinner.

Judge Cooper saw the transfiguration. The erstwhile moping collie won, on the strength of it; and was recorded duly as a champion. Less than a year thereafter Judge Cooper and Wolf and Treve all three were dead. This rotten old world has lots of room in it for the digging of graves. Hasn't it?

Treve was, as I have told you, the most obedient dog I have owned. He understood and obeyed my lightest whispered command.

When we marched into the show ring together he would carry his tail high above his back—an unpardonable show fault. He would glance sidewise at me in defiance, as he did so. I would whisper: "Tail *down!*" Down would go the tail, to the correct angle. But at the same time Treve would growl murderously and he would grab my hand in his white teeth—in a bite whose pressure was not a tenth of an ounce.

Judge and exhibitors and spectators would edge away from the ferociously savage brute.

On the judging block he would turn one of his fore paws deliberately inward, which is another heinous show fault. I would whisper: "Paw *out!*" Again he obeyed me, at once. But again with that same wild-beast growl and with a grabbing of my hand or wrist. Again, too, that murmur of dread from the bystanders, and the prudent edging away of other exhibitors.

The judge would look askance at him, in trepidation, when the time came to "go over" Treve. I would say ingratiatingly:

"He's perfectly gentle, Judge. It's only his idea of a joke."

Timidly or wrathfully, the judge would begin to examine him. Almost invariably Treve would bite him. And the judge would blink foolishly at his own unpierced and unhurt hand. It is a miracle the collie ever won his championship. He did all he could to make the judges keep him from winning.

Not once in all his brief life did Treve show any mark of affection for me, beyond a daily burying of his head between my knees as I sat writing. This to an accompaniment of hideous growls and of threatened bites.

Yet whenever I went to town for the day, he would

watch the car out of sight. Then he would go to the hall table, and take my cap from it.

Into my study he would slink, with head and tail drooping in sick dejection. He would lie there miserably all day, the cap between his fore paws. He would roar in ferocious menace at anyone, except the Mistress, who might venture near to the study door.

On my return to Sunnybank, that night, he would pay no slightest attention to me. He seemed to be unaware of my presence. He would toss the cap back on the hall table, and trot out to romp with the other dogs.

He loved that study of mine above all places in his narrow world. When he was about a year old he had a short but horribly dangerous illness. For two days and nights I sat up with him in the study; soothing him with my voice when he was suffering, feeding him and giving him his nasty medicines.

After that it was Treve's study. Not mine.

Whenever he was indoors he went thither, as by divine right. There he would lie down, in proprietory majesty. He would snarl and bark and shriek threats at any and every other dog who chanced to come within six feet of the door. If the Mistress or myself entered the study, he greeted us hospitably; though with the air of one who admits favored guests to his own jealously protected abode.

Woe to any other members of the Sunnybank household or to any guest who might venture into the study! My daughter dropped in on me there, one day, in her bathing suit; on her way to the lake. Treve charged at her, growling mortal defiance.

He bit her fervidly and repeatedly on her bare feet and ankles and calves; striving the while to shoulder her out into the hallway. She complained to me, in some natural annoyance:

"I wish Treve wouldn't do that, whenever I come in here. He *tickles* so, when he bites!"

The Mistress was the only human of his acquaintance whom Treve never attempted to bite. I don't know why; except that all our Sunnybank dogs, from the first, have treated her with a queer reverent gentleness and affection which they have bestowed on nobody else.

Treve used to cuddle at her feet and go to sleep, as she sat reading by the fire in the armor-hung living room. Suddenly, with a roar of fury, he would awaken, baring his teeth at her as she sat above him. She would laugh, and say:

"You've had such a *nice* nap, Trevy! And now you've waked up in a beautiful homicidal rage!"

The dog would sigh plaintively, at her lack of fear; and he would go to sleep again with his head on her foot.

She wrote a little song in which his name appeared several times. Treve used to lure her to the piano by tugging softly at the hem of her skirt. There, head on one side in critical enjoyment, he would stand listening; as long as he could persuade her to repeat the song.

He had a rare love for her music. He would come at a dead run to the music room as soon as he heard the Mistress strike a chord on the piano. And he would stay there for hours, if need be, until she had finished playing. If anyone but herself touched the piano he would drown the performance in a fanfare of disgusted barks.

Let's get away from Sunnybank for a little while, and into the news columns.

In Metowah, Tenn., dwelt a bloodhound so astute at his thief-catching profession that he was known as Sherlock Holmes, Jr. He belonged to Deputy

SHERLOCK HOLMES, JR

Sheriff Roy Carver. A Negro of sporting tastes, Butler by name, vanished from the town. By some odd coincidence, at the same time, a costly motorcar was reported missing.

Sheriff Carver put two and two together to such effect that he set off in search of Butler. He loosed Sherlock Holmes on the trail. Whereat, the bloodhound disappeared as mystifyingly and as completely as had Butler and the automobile.

After a long time, Carver got word of his errant

hound. He found that Sherlock Holmes, Jr, had not only run Butler to earth, but had adopted the Negro as his master. The sheriff caught up with the pair, just as Butler had taught the bloodhound the practical art of tracking rabbits for him.

The trail-following man hunter had become happily engrossed in this new and more congenial job. He resented his former master's efforts to wean him from it. The dog found it vastly pleasanter to aid his car-addicted black friend in running rabbits to earth than to track human criminals.

In New Castle, Pa., a freak police dog upheaved the city government and was the basis of a change in municipal mastership. His name was Tag. The local newspapers branded him as "The Judas Dog." He belonged to the New Castle poundmaster and dogcatcher, John E. Young, a former pugilist.

Tag was a quick learner. Young was a good teacher. But never could the man have taught the police dog to ply his trade so brilliantly, unless Tag had been fitted for it by some quirk of his own clever brain.

Here is a rough idea of the job learned or evolved by Tag:

To betray his fellow dogs into the dogcatcher's net.

For every dog caught and taken to the pound, the city paid Young a small fee. Every impounded dog not claimed within a certain time was put to death. Young received an extra fee of $2.00 for these killings. It was much to his interest, therefore, to catch and kill as many dogs as he could.

But the average stray or tramp dog has learned

caution from much ill-experience with mankind. Such dogs were hard to catch.

Then there were other dogs—chum dogs—which could not be grabbed while they were on their owners' land; but which were Young's legitimate prey if they should wander into the street without muzzle and leash.

Few house dogs are muzzled or leashed while they are at home. Nor are they easy to lure from their home grounds.

But Tag solved both these difficulties for his master.

Young and the police dog would ride through the residence streets on the seat of the pound's truck. Tag's eyes raked the neighborhood on either side. At sight of a tramp dog eating out of a corner garbage can, he would bark under his breath.

Young would stop the truck. Tag would hop down to the ground. Stealthily he would creep up to the unsuspecting garbage eater. Young, net or noose in hand, stayed in the background; out of sight.

If the dog to be captured were small enough, Tag pinned him to the curb and held them there while Young ran up and caught him. In the case of a larger stray dog, Tag would engage him in a romp or else in a fight; to keep him from noticing Young until the noose or the net had done its work.

A wholly different and more subtle method was called for in catching house dogs. And here Tag's lopsided genius came into its own.

A dog was sleeping on its owner's porch or in the door-yard. Tag frisked up to him, in blithe friendliness, urging him to play. If the dog accepted the invitation, Tag maneuvered the ensuing frolic's course gradually out into the street; where Young and Young's noose were waiting.

If the house dog declined to play, Tag broke into wild insulting barks, challenging him to battle. As he was barking, he was backing away as if in fear. Few dogs can resist a chance like that; to go for a cur which is defying them on their own land and yet is patently afraid.

Always the house dog rushed at Tag. Always Tag retreated in craven terror. Always Tag guided the line of retreat out into the road and straight to Young.

It was a mighty lucrative trade for the poundmaster. It was grand fun for his Judas dog. While it lasted.

But trouble was coming in their direction. It was coming fast and with much punitive power.

Mrs Elizabeth Fisher, a schoolteacher, looked out of a front window of her home; as Tag was coaxing her fluffy little poodle, Tony, off the lawn and to the edge of the curb. As the dogs reached the street she heard Young say:

"*Hold* him, Tag!"

The police dog ceased frolicking at this command. He pounced on the unsuspecting poodle and held him down until Young could finish the capture. Mrs Fisher ran out and rescued Tony, barely in time to save him from a ride to the pound. Then she complained to the mayor of Newcastle. She told the story everywhere.

Other complaints came pouring into the city hall.

The town was roused. The local Humane Society took action, denouncing Young's methods and decreeing it was illegal to use one dog to catch another. Young denied that any cruelty was involved.

"Tag never musses them up when he brings them in," he told the reporters. "I've trained him not to."

Then the papers printed the experiences of another of Tag's victims. Gigolo, a Samoyed, belonged to Mrs Robert Gorst, a crippled woman with an invalid husband. Tag enticed Gigolo into the street and into Young's noose, and the luckless Samoyed was trundled to the pound.

This affair fanned white hot the flame of public indignation. There was a civic upheaval. A new mayor was elected, though there was no reason to think the former city authorities had any knowledge of Tag's Judas tactics; much less connived at them.

The new mayor fired Young from his job. He held up a bill for $126, in $2.00 bonuses, which the poundmaster declared was due him for killing unclaimed dogs.

So Tag lost the one form of livelihood he had been taught; the freakiest and slimiest form of livelihood, I think, that any dog could take up.

At the renowned Alstead Collie Kennels, in Rahway, N. J., was born a listlessly melancholy tricolor (black, white and tan) pup of glorious show points but apparently of no dash or semblance of spirit.

He was registered as "Alstead Aeroplane," a name which now adorns the pedigrees of innumerable show collies.

SOME FREAK DOGS

People regarded Aeroplane as a born fool. But he was not. He was only apathetic, because never had he been roused. Fine qualities lurked in the back of his brain, and never had they been brought to life.

Always, I denied that he was a fool. And I based my denial on a freakish accomplishment of his. It was this:

Daily, the Alstead collies were let out of their pens for exercise. A few of them made friends with young Aeroplane. Most of them did not. One or two of them used to go for him. Aeroplane learned at once which dogs were his playmates and well-wishers and which were not.

After all of them had been put back into their pens, Aeroplane, with no trouble at all, would unfasten the somewhat intricate catch of his kennel door and would trot out into the open.

Thence he went to the pens of his few comrades and unfastened the latches or drop bolts. Out would gallop these liberated collies. They and Aeroplane would frisk about the grounds together until they were discovered and put back.

Never would he let out any of the collies except his own friends.

Now, I felt certain that this was not by any means the action of a fool; apart from Aeroplane's uncanny gift for unfastening door catches of all kinds. Somewhere in such a dog there was a latent greatness. Events proved I was right.

In spite of his listlessness in and out of the show ring, Aeroplane was of such superb physical quality that he won his way to a championship in an unusually short time. He caught the fancy of Alex Donaldson, a Toronto collie fancier.

Donaldson bought him at a goodly price, and took him to Toronto.

There he put the young champion in a kennel yard, for the night. A yard with ordinary fastenings on its gate.

In the morning, Aeroplane was gone.

Perhaps his new owner did not know the dog's genius at latch picking. Or perhaps he did not believe. In any case, he had lost his high-priced and higher-quality collie.

This is what had happened:

Aeroplane had let himself out of his prison yard. Thence, he had made his way out of the city; and far into the neighboring countryside, to a stretch of woodland. In the woods was the wreck of an old dance floor, on what once had been a picnic ground.

There was a hole under the raised and rotted flooring. Aeroplane crawled in through it. He made that place his lair for the next ten months.

Of course, there arose the vital question of food.

Remember, Aeroplane's carefully balanced rations had been served to him since babyhood at regular hours and in a sanitary feed dish. He never had done any foraging for himself. He had not so much as caught a mouse or rifled a garbage pail.

To all outward appearances, he was as helpless to fend for himself as would be a human child of the same age.

Yet for the best part of a year, thereafter, he lived on the fat of the land. He solved the food problem as readily as he had solved the door-latch problem.

He robbed hen roosts and lamb folds for a radius of miles. He learned to stalk wild game in the woods; even as his wolf ancestors had taught it to their cubs.

When the average dog catches a hen, the noise of squawking and flapping can be heard all over the farm. But when a fox or a wolf kills a fowl the deed is done in complete silence. The victim is caught in such a way that it cannot flutter or make any outcry.

Aeroplane taught himself this strange accomplishment of the wild. Also, his knack of unfastening door catches stood him in good stead when he came to a shut chicken coop or a farmyard or barn. The most puzzling and intricate latches held no difficulty for him.

How did he teach himself to do all these things? The answer is: He didn't.

The long-buried instinct of the wild came to life in that freak brain of his; came to life the first moment he had need to call on it. The pampered parasite became all at once an inspired creature of the wilderness. Which is a miracle by itself.

Through the bitter Canadian winter the dog throve amazingly. His coat took on an unheard-of thickness and luster. His lean body filled out to the mighty strength of a timber wolf's.

The hue and cry was after him, by reason of his wholesale depredations. And again grim old Mother Nature whispered to his awakened brain a secret of the wild. He learned to double on his tracks and to confuse his trail as adroitly as ever did a wolf or a fox.

He shook off pursuit, without once being seen. He

learned the man smell and to keep away from its vicinity; as a million savage forest beasts have done.

Early one morning, he met a wandering and warlike billygoat near the edge of the road. The dog tried to kill him, for food. Men came along, just as the goat was qualifying for admission to the highly scented Capricorn heaven. They chased Aeroplane. So close were they to him that he had no time or chance to hide. To his lair he ran. There after a hot struggle he was noosed and muzzled.

For three days and nights he stood trembling and dejected in a stockade Donaldson built for him. Then, cheerily, he took up the burden of civilized life.

I owned two of his best children. A fourth-generation descendant of his, my Sunnybank King Coal, is Aeroplane's living image except for the lack of some of his ancestor's physical perfection.

King Coal is rolling on the grass beside me, as I write this. I did not let him out of his yard. He let himself out. He inherits that astonishing talent of Aeroplane's for working loose any simple latch or bolt.

Roger was a bloodhound. He belonged to the Reverend Morton Leslie who had a church in a suburb of Liverpool, England. Every Sunday, Roger went to church with his master. There he lay quietly at the foot of the pulpit stairs, throughout the service. He was daft about churchgoing.

One Sunday Mr Leslie had a bad sore throat and could not speak above a whisper. So he sat in one of the pews, while a colleague from another parish undertook to preach in his stead. As usual, Roger lay at the foot of the pulpit as the services began.

But when the stranger started to mount the pulpit stairs, the bloodhound yelled with murderous wrath and went at him; throwing him to the floor. There was a terrible scene. At its conclusion, Mr Leslie led Roger home in black disgrace.

The dog seemed to realize that he had done wrong. For never again did he follow his master to church.

But, a month later, Mr Leslie was accosted in the street by an infuriated woman, a Mrs Harris, who was prominent in a chapel in the suburb—a chapel whose members carried on a long-time feud with those of Mr Leslie's church.

Mrs Harris demanded now of the bewildered clergyman what he meant by insulting her religion and her place of worship. She went on ragingly:

"You've trained that hulking savage brute of a Roger to come to our chapel every single Sunday morning and every single Sunday evening, and to lie down at the foot of the pulpit. He breaks up the services, just by being there.

"And he snarls at us when we try to put him out. But we're going to law about it!"

Quite at a loss to understand what it all was about, Mr Leslie sought out the clergyman in charge of Mrs Harris' chapel. He learned that the angry woman's statement was true—as far as it concerned Roger's presence at services.

Every Sunday, since the day of his disgrace, the

bloodhound had traveled, morning and evening, all the way to the chapel; and he had taken up his lifelong place at the foot of the pulpit. Ashamed to go to his old-time church, yet craving to attend divine services, Roger had gone to the other denomination's pulpit foot.

Grip was a mongrel. He belonged to Tom Gerrard, an eighteenth-century London thief of much notoriety in his day. The dog had a rare knowledge of the smell of leather. And he made a rare use of that knowledge. He would go wagging and wriggling up to some well-dressed man, in the streets, coaxing to be petted. Usually the man would stoop down to stroke the friendly cur's head.

As he did so, Grip's sharp sense of smell would locate the stranger's leathern wallet. With a lightning-quick jerk of the head he would snatch the pocketbook; and then would take to his heels and vanish around a corner. The dog did not stop running until he reached his master's room. There he would thrust the stolen wallet into Tom Gerrard's hand.

Presently, Gerrard aspired to a nobler place in his chosen trade. He gave up picking pockets—for which he had brilliant aptitude—for the profession of highwayman, for which he had so little aptitude that in August of 1711 he was caught and hanged.

As poor masterless Grip roamed the streets disconsolately he attracted the notice of the Rev. Dr Burgess, a Presbyterian clergyman. Out of pity for the forlorn animal the clergyman took him home and kept him. Soon, Grip had learned to love his new owner almost as much as he had loved Gerrard. And he yearned to serve him in the same practical way.

One day Dr Burgess went into a shop to make a number of purchases. He left Grip outside to wait for him. When he emerged at last the dog thrust into his hand a wallet containing some silver and a few coppers. The man supposed Grip had picked up the wallet in the street somewhere. He advertised it. There was no reply. So he turned the handful of coins over to his church's Poor Fund.

Two days later Burgess went to pay a long pastoral call on a sick parishioner. As before, Grip was left to wait outside. And as before, the dog greeted his emerging master by putting into his hand another wallet; this one almost bursting with banknotes and gold sovereigns.

The same thing happened again, next day.

Now, any dog might well have picked up a wallet from the pavement. But it was not likely any dog could pick up three wallets inside of a week. Dr Burgess told the odd story to friends of his. One of these friends chanced to tell it to a London police official. The official carried the news to Scotland Yard.

Constables, who had known Tom Gerrard and Tom Gerrard's dog, called on Dr Burgess. Immediately they recognized Grip as the freak mongrel with the talent for wallet snatching.

In horror at such iniquity, the clergyman hanged the dog to a tree in his back garden.

British dogs, since earliest days, had been put to death by hanging. So perhaps Burgess' treatment of Grip was less barbarous than it sounds. Let's hope so.

Yet the unhappy brute had done nothing, consciously, to merit death.

We taught Sunnybank Gray Dawn to go to the gateway and get the two morning papers and to bring them down here to the house. We made the mistake of praising him extravagantly for this simple exploit. And praise ever went to Dawn's head, like alcohol.

The next morning we found twenty-six newspapers piled in a disordered heap on the veranda.

Eager to win even higher praise, Dawn had gone throughout the neighborhood, on our own side of the lake; and he had collected and brought home every morning paper he could find at porch or doorway.

A dozen more of Gray Dawn's freak performances are recorded at greater length in my book bearing his name. Among them his treatment of a gold-banded dog whip which had flicked him lightly over the hips when, as a half-grown pup, he had torn a lace handkerchief to shreds.

Dawn dug a deep hole in a heliotrope bed; dropped the punitive whip into the excavation; and shoved the earth in on top of it.

Never again could that stinging scourge molest him. Dawn had made very certain of that.

CHAPTER XI

Some Hero Dogs

WHEN I WAS A CHILD, I stood in front of a badly stuffed yellowish St Bernard dog in the Swiss museum at Berne. My father had told me the badly stuffed carcass had been Barry's. And he had told me the story of Barry.

As I stared at the wretchedly poor bit of taxidermy, I had to remind myself that I was a man, six years old; and that six-year-old men are hardboiled and are not supposed to cry.

Probably you know Barry's story as well as I do. But it will do you no harm to read the grand tale again. So here it is:

For centuries before Progress bored a tunnel under the giant mountain, a pass connected France with Switzerland and Italy.

(In my childhood, a *diligence* drawn by scraggy horses used to drag my parents and me over the summit. I used to get out there in midsummer, during the changing of horses, to make snowballs, and to throw them at the postilions who swore back at me in a barbarous patois. As a man I have ridden often through a smoky hole in the base of the mountain on a cindery train and in a glum dimness. I prefer the pass to the tunnel.)

Near the crest of the pass, the Monastery of St Bernard was established, in 962 A.D., with its hospice for mountain travelers. As the treacherous pass was snow-swept much of the year, foot passengers used to lose their way or collapse from cold and from blizzard.

Therefore "the pious monks of St. Bernard" trained a corps of strong and oversized yellowish dogs to go out from the hospice, by night or in storm, to guide pedestrians to the safety of warm rooms and good food and comfortable lodgings.

The thousand-year line of gallant lifesaving St Bernard dogs—dogs especially bred and evolved and developed, to make each generation better than the last—contains many an immortal name. But above all the rest stands out the name of Barry.

Barry was born at the St Bernard hospice in 1800. He took to the rigorous course of training with eager delight. He learned faster than any of his fellow pupils. He did more: He displayed psychic powers in his work—powers hard to explain, and therefore attributed to instinct and to heredity. It was this psychic gift that saved lives, and at last brought him to his death.

During his first ten years, Barry rescued no fewer than forty Alpine travelers from perishing in the snow.

One of these was a lost child who had wandered off the pass and was overtaken by a blizzard. Instinct—not the monks' orders—sent Barry out of the hospice and through a mile of snow to find the youngster.

How he knew of her peril and where to look for her, is beyond any mere human's guess.

But he made his way unerringly to where she lay half-unconscious in the storm. He licked her icy face and cuddled close to her, so that she might receive warmth from his shaggy body.

When the little girl was able to move, he coaxed her in some way of his own to climb on his back. And in this fashion he carried her safely to the hospice.

The career of a lifesaving St Bernard dog never has been easy, and seldom long. In those days it took grueling toll of strength and endurance. Hospice dogs wore out early.

Barry was an exception. Yet when he was ten, the monks retired the old fellow from active duty and kept him on at the hospice as an honored pensioner. There were younger, if lesser, dogs to carry on his task. So for another five years Barry lived in lazy contentment.

Then of a winter night in 1815, a snowstorm was raging across the pass. In the hospice kitchen old Barry snoozed in front of the fire.

He found it monstrous pleasant, no doubt, to loaf like this in the ruddy warmth of the hearth while the storm yelled around the ancient stone walls and the snow's sharp fingers scratched at the window glass; to know his own hard life work was done, and so gloriously done, and that he could revel henceforth in the lazy rest he had earned; to know supper soon would be ready and that a snug night's sleep lay ahead of him.

There was a short lull in the howl of the storm. In that moment of stillness, Barry started wide awake.

He scrambled to his feet as fast as his rheumatic old muscles would let him. To the door he ran. There he scratched vehemently at the panels.

Someone opened the door for him to go out; not guessing that his mysterious instinct had shouted an S O S message to his deafening ears. Into the storm bounded the great dog, and down the pass. He ran almost with his early speed; he whose fastest pace, for the last five years, had been a leisurely jog-trot.

On he galloped until he came upon a figure half-buried in the drifting snow.

A soldier had been crossing the pass, and had lost his way in the blizzard. Exhausted, drugged by the bitter cold, he had fallen headlong into a drift; and he lay there.

The soldier was roused from his coma by something that licked his face. He opened his eyes. There, standing over him and bulking gigantic in the dim light, was a hairy creature of some kind.

The soldier screamed in panic terror, thinking the beast was a wolf. Scourged by that insanity of fear, he whipped a knife from his belt. And he plunged the weapon, hilt-deep, in Barry's side.

The dog must have known he had received his own death blow. But he had no time to die, while this man's life was in peril. Back to the hospice he jogged, with what speed he could muster; leaving a trail of blood in the snow at every step.

He gave the alarm to the monks. Then he led them to where the freezing soldier lay. The man was taken to the hospice. His life was saved.

Then and only then could Barry collapse. The man

AND IN THIS FASHION BARRY CARRIED HER SAFELY

who had killed him was safe. There was no longer any reason why the dog should not allow himself the luxury of slipping out of pain and out of life.

Do you blame me because at the age of six, I had trouble swallowing the lump in my young throat when I heard Barry's story and looked on Barry's badly stuffed hide?

Here is a true story which received much newspaper space a few years ago—a story which seems to me to deserve retelling, in our chapter about hero dogs:

André Minette was a master woodsman. He lived in a forest clearing not far from Seguin Falls, in Canada. He lived there with his wife and their baby son, Jean, and a big crossbreed dog named Sport.

Sport had a high and gory repute as the best wolf hunter in the region. In his own mixed breeding there was a strong strain of wolf—a strain which gave him not only great strength and speed, but also the wiliness and the inspired battle tactics of a timber wolf.

The average timber wolf can thrash and kill the average dog of anywhere near its own size. But Sport was not the average dog, thanks to that same wolf strain. More than once he had outfought a wolf.

And he had the craftiness to avoid mixing into a scrimmage with two or more wolves at a time. He knew well that this would be a sure and painful form of suicide for him. So he met his wolf foes singly. And he steered clear of the pack.

Minette used to be away from home for days at a time, on camping trips for his timber industry. He had no fear in leaving his wife and child in his wilderness house, during these absences. Sport was an all-efficient and all-vigilant protector.

The big dog dedicated himself to the loving service of Baby Jean. Never when he could help it would he let the child out of his sight. His devotion to Jean was beautiful.

One morning in early spring, Minette was with a logging gang on a hill not very far from the house. His wife wheeled the baby's perambulator out into a patch of sunlight at one end of the clearing. She left Jean there with Sport on guard, while she went back to her housework.

It had been a hard winter. Game had been scarce. The wolves had come closer to civilized places than usual, made recklessly bold by starvation.

This morning three gaunt timber wolves slunk out from the shelter of the forest and into the Minette clearing. Sport was on his feet, at first distant scent of them. Grimly he stood guard over the baby.

Well must he have known no dog ever lived that could maintain its own in a battle against three such wolves. But he held his ground.

Easily he might have darted for safety into the open doorway of the house behind him. But that would have left Jean to the mercy of the merciless; to the teeth of the famishing wolves.

Just then Minette came in sight, on his way home from the hill. At a glance he saw and understood the black horror of the situation. But he was too far away to reach the baby carriage and its tiny occupant. And he had no gun with him that day. He could only look on, frozen with dread.

He could see the three wolves mass for an attack, as Sport ran at them. The dog was not charging in blind fury. He was using every atom of that wily brain of his. He was there to throw away his own bright life. But he was not going to throw it away in vain.

If he should hurl himself frantically at the wolves, two of them could destroy him with ease; while the third should seize Jean and drag the baby into the woods. This death battle must be waged as cunningly as a championship chess match.

Minette told of what followed, to a newspaper correspondent for the London *Express*. I am going to quote from the *Express'* account. It tells the rest of Sport's story better than could words of mine:

"The dog sparred like a prize fighter with his snarling opponents. After edging about for a minute or so, Sport had the three wolves with their backs to the baby; and he himself was backing into the woods.

"Dog and wolves alike seemed afraid to strike the first blow. Then suddenly Sport turned tail to his foes and dashed off into the forest, as if in terror. The three gray-coated wolves followed hard at his heels.

"The dog never returned. But he had accomplished what he had endeavored to do: he had led the wolves away from the baby's perambulator."

I said it was a battle that called for brain work and not for brute force. And Sport had the brain to do the only thing which could have saved Jean from being torn to pieces and devoured.

One can picture that race through the spring forest, with the dog carefully keeping just far enough ahead of his pursuers to lure them on. Then of their final overhauling of him when his speed began to fail; and of the ghastly combat that changed into slaughter.

It is not a pretty picture, perhaps. But it is the last phase of a life sacrifice; made, gladly, in order that a child might live. To me, there is something more than Homeric—something sublime—about it.

Into only a short space I shall crowd another story of the same general trend as Sport's. A story too illustrious to omit from any chronicle of dog heroes. Perhaps there are none of you who don't know the tale as well as I do. It is the saga of Gelert.

King John of England tried to win the loyalty of Llewellyn, most powerful and most troublesome of the several turbulent Welsh princes. So the king gave his own royal daughter, the Princess Joanna, to Llewellyn in marriage. For a wedding gift he sent his new son-in-law the finest staghound in the realm—a hound known to history and to song as Gelert.

Llewellyn accepted both the bride and the dog. But he seems to have been much fonder and much prouder of Gelert than of Joanna. When the chief's first son was born, the dog elected himself to the office of perpetual guardian to the baby.

He lay in the castle's nursery beside the infant's cot, day and night, rather than go hunting with his master.

Llewellyn was glad enough to have such an incorruptibly valiant guard for his child. For he and King John had just had a terrific quarrel, and the king had threatened to strike at the chief through the latter's son.

It was an age of assassinations and of bestial cruelty. King John was an adept at both.

One day a wolf crept in through the unglazed nursery casement, while the baby was asleep. The brute was maddened by hunger. He was on his stealthy way to the cot when Gelert tackled him. There was a short battle. Both animals were badly slashed.

Gelert killed the wolf; and he stood above the crib once more on guard.

Just then, Llewellyn came home from the hunt. As he entered the nursery he saw the baby lying in the cot, as if dead. The little fellow's face and clothes were smeared thick with blood. Over him stood Gelert, blood dripping from his slashed jaws. The scene apparently told its own hideous story: the story of a child murdered by a rabid dog.

Llewellyn's long-bladed knife split Gelert's heart in halves.

Then the baby awoke and began to cry. At the same time Llewellyn saw the mangled body of the wolf sprawling behind the cot.

He buried the hero hound with almost royal honors —not that that benefited the poor victim in any way— and he named the land around the tomb in Gelert's honor. To this day, the village that stands on the site is called "Beddgelert"—Welsh for "Gelert's Grave."

Malakoff was a Newfoundland. He was owned by a wholesale jeweler in Paris, who named his dog for the spectacular French victory over the Russians in 1855. The dog had a keen zest for practical jokes.

Also he was a most incurable fighter. Both traits led to endless trouble.

Malakoff would wander lazily up and down the street in front of his master's shop, until some well-dressed man walked past. Then, Malakoff would be so awkward as to get in the pedestrian's way. In disengaging himself from the collision the dog usually would manage to get between the man's legs, and upset him into the mud of the gutter.

He would leap playfully upon well-dressed children, too, sending them off balance and into the gutter mud.

His master had several apprentices. It was Malakoff's joy in life to tease them and to play jokes on them. They hated him. More and more they craved a safe chance to get rid of him. Their opportunity came, one day when the Newfoundland staggered into the shop, torn and cut and in woeful condition.

He had been out on one of his cherished fighting tours. As he and a mastiff were battling avidly, several of the mastiff's canine friends joined in the fray. They "ganged" Malakoff; to such an extent that he could scarcely crawl home.

He lay down, bleeding and worn out, in a dark corner of the shop. He growled feebly at all who came near.

The apprentices went into a huddle. Then Jacques, the ringleader, ran to a friend of his, whom he bribed to call himself a veterinary.

The pseudo-vet earned his dirty fee in short order. He pretended to examine Malakoff. He assured the shop's proprietor that the Newfoundland had rabies,

SOME HERO DOGS 293

and must be put to death at once, before he could bite some human.

The scared proprietor agreed. Jacques and his fellow apprentices came forward with an offer to drown the dog in the Seine. Sadly Malakoff's master assented. He was badly frightened. He had a horror of rabies. So he told his apprentices to go ahead with the execution.

Jacques lassoed Malakoff's shaggy throat, from one side, while another apprentice did the same thing on his other side. They dragged the helplessly protesting dog to the end of the nearest pier that jutted out into the river. It was wintertime. The water was icy cold and it was in flood.

While two apprentices held Malakoff securely at either end of the impromptu lassos, Jacques tied a heavy stone to a rope; and fastened the rope's free end around Malakoff's neck. To make doubly certain of his drowning, they wrapped one of the lasso ropes tightly around his fore legs.

Jacques gave the poor brute a mighty shove; sending him heels over head down into the river.

The forward plunge of the Newfoundland's falling body dislodged the end of the lasso rope. The rope, in snapping loose, whipped itself around Jacques's ankle.

Over toppled the dog drowner into the ice-chill water. Incidentally, he never had taken the trouble to learn to swim.

Deep beneath the surface went Jacques. As he came up, gasping and floundering impotently, another and larger head emerged from the river a few feet away from him.

The apprentice had miscalculated the Newfoundland's great strength. The stone he had selected was heavy, but not heavy enough to drag so powerful a swimmer to the bottom at once.

Up came Malakoff, struggling with the weight of the rock around his neck. Lucky it was for him that the lasso rope had snapped loose from around his legs. Yet the stone was tugging at him. He was in much pain. The blood lost in that day's wholesale battle had weakened him.

He was striking out wearily for shore, dragging the stone behind him on its length of rope, and trying to stem the swift current, when he caught sight of Jacques.

The apprentice was going down for the second time, while his fellows at the edge of the pier above him bawled vainly for help.

It was then that Malakoff rated a place for himself in our hero-dog chapter.

Calling on all his waning strength, the dog clove his way through the flood to where Jacques's head was vanishing beneath the surface. Gripping the half-drowned apprentice by the coat collar, Malakoff lifted his face clear of the water.

Then he made for shore again, towing the man who had tried to kill him.

The Newfoundland could not have failed to know of Jacques's leading share in the execution; from the lassoing and the dragging of the dog to the pier, to the stone-tying and the final shove over the edge.

But that had been Jacques's responsibility. Not Malakoff's. The dog's one job just now was to save this would-be slayer's life.

It is no light thing to tow a helpless and squirming man to shore, through flood-swollen waters; even for a Newfoundland that is not handicapped in any way. But when loss of blood and the incessant pulling back of a stone are added as impediments, the going is increasingly hard. As Malakoff found out.

By letting go of Jacques's coat collar and leaving the wretched apprentice to drown, he would have been able to gain the bank. He must have known this, too. But he would not let go.

He was making pitifully little progress.

Then presently he was making no progress at all. For a crosscurrent was pulling him back toward the center of the river. He fought on, with what ebbing vitality he had. And his grip on the apprentice's collar never slackened.

At last a boat was rowed out from shore. Jacques and the dog were hauled aboard. Both of them were more dead than alive.

Jacques was as full of remorse as of river water. He told the story to everyone he met. So did the apprentices who had watched from the end of the pier. In a week it was all over Paris.

Jacques's father insisted on buying the Newfoundland for his son. The dog was the hero of the whole city.

In 1862 Malakoff died. It is recorded that almost every apprentice in Paris begged for time off from work, to attend the dog's burial. Long before that time the city's throng of apprentices had grown to look on him as a sort of Patron Saint of their guild.

I am going to end this chapter and our book with the true tale of a hero dog of Sunnybank—a dog I bred and owned. Perhaps you have read it before. For it "made the front page" of all the metropolitan newspapers, back in 1923; and it is told in a book of mine which bears its hero's name.

The dog was Wolf—Sunnybank Wolf, a fiery little red-gold collie, son of great Sunnybank Lad.

Wolf belonged to the Mistress. To her and to me, in the order named, he was a steadfast chum. To the world at large he was indifferent. As long as the world at large would consent to leave him alone.

When members of the world at large undertook to pet him or to annoy him in any way (and tenfold so if they came up to the car where he and the Mistress sat side by side) he became a wild beast; with all the swift and deadly savagery of a leopard.

He was the fiercest dog we have owned. And one of the most lovable—to the only two people he loved.

He had more common sense, by far, than has the average dog. He used to reason things out in a queerly human way. For example:

A litter of three-months collie pups took silly pleasure in selecting the center of our driveway as a playground. This used to worry Wolf. Not that he had any affection for those pups or for any other puppies. But because they were so stupidly helpless.

When they were lying or playing in the driveway, Wolf kept a watchful eye on them. The moment a car or a truck turned in from the highroad and started down the drive, he was up and among the group of fluffy youngsters.

As skillfully as any trained sheep dog, he would bunch them and set them into fast motion, herding them off the spot of danger and into the woods at one side, before the vehicle could reach them.

We used to praise him for this. And he was egregiously flattered and tickled by our praise.

One day when a car was coming down the drive toward the clumsily playing pups, Wolf was too far away to round up and herd the babies as usual. So he broke into a riotous volley of barking—most provocative and excited barking—and went galloping past the pups; at the same time veering sharply into the woods.

No normal pup could have resisted the thrilling invitation in that bark. It said as clearly as words:

"Come on, everybody! After *me!* There's grand fun ahead!"

Every one of the fool puppies cantered after him as fast as their legs would propel them. Off the drive they scuttled in Wolf's wake; and barely in time to avoid the oncoming car.

Even more fulsomely did we praise him for this stunt; involving as it did a bit of clever thinking. (I wish now we had thrashed him every time he tried to save a pup or a grown dog from being run over. He would have lived longer. For our praise imbedded the rescue impulse deep into his queer brain.)

He could take long hikes, unaccompanied by any of us, on motor-infested roads. His amazing caution and sense, and his uncanny judgment of speed and of distances, kept him as safe on such roads as in one of our own meadows.

From a distance, too, as he was on a walk with us, in his youth, he saw a small dog cut in two by a railroad train. Thereafter, untaught by anyone, he would halt before crossing a railroad track. He would peer anxiously in both directions to make certain no train was near.

On a June day in 1923, when Wolf was about ten years old, my auburn house collie, Bobby—nearly twice Wolf's size—was asleep at the bottom of the driveway, not far from the veranda where we were sitting. None of us noticed the approach of a delivery truck, until it came around a thicket of shrubs, at high speed, just in front of where Bobby slept.

Wolf flashed forward. He caught the slowly waking Bobby by the shoulder and, by main force, slung him aside, out of danger. Then, with lightning quickness and with his perfect judgment of distance and of timing, Wolf dodged out of the way of the truck.

For perhaps the fiftieth time in the past decade I announced loudly that one day he would be killed.

I did not believe my own prediction. I knew his skill and his speed. And I trusted in them. Otherwise I should have been acutely worried. For the fiery little red-gold collie had made himself unsparably dear to the Mistress and to me.

That evening before bedtime Wolf sauntered forth on one of his nightly walks of an hour's duration. He neared the railroad track, a mile or so from Sunnybank. Seven people were sitting on the handkerchief-sized porches of cottages and bungalows along the far side of the track. Above, three electric lights made the rails vividly visible.

It was from the unanimous testimony of these seven persons that I gleaned the true tale of what ensued.

Wolf trotted up to the tracks, with his elusively fast mile-eating choppy gait. There as always he halted, glancing up and down the line of double rails.

A light came into view behind the curve of the track, a quarter mile to northward. Wolf stepped backward until the Stroudsburg Express—some minutes late and trying to make up for lost time—should roar past.

It was then that Wolf saw a nondescript little mongrel amble out onto the tracks. The mongrel sat down between the rails to scratch an importunate flea. Around the bend came the belated express.

Wolf sprang, barking, at the mongrel. The latter shambled to its feet and cowered in mid track; blinking with dazzled eyes at the headlight of the onrushing locomotive.

The flea-ravaged cur was stupefied by the noisy approach of the train. It crouched trembling between the gleaming rails.

Then, as a score of times before, Wolf went into action.

He barked a second raucous warning. The mongrel gave no heed to his admonition, but continued to shiver helplessly between the rails. The headlight waxed brighter and more confusing.

A locomotive whistle split the silence of the night, completing the mongrel's paralysis of fear. The brute cringed, moveless, impotent, in the path of the whizzing train.

Forward Wolf flung himself. He grasped the mongrel by the nape of the neck, as the locomotive's cowcatcher loomed just above. In the super-canine burst of strength he flung the cur far down into the track-side ditch.

Then Wolf leaped backward.

He missed the engine itself. But a bit of metal, far to one side of it, kissed the corner of his skull.

The onlookers telephoned to me. I drove to the scene of rescue. There, with not a scar nor a fleck of blood on his splendid red-gold body, lay Wolf—peacefully asleep. Asleep for all time.

"Others he saved. Himself he could not save."

Wolf had done what all his life, under our foolish praise, he had trained himself to do. And well he had known the awful risk he ran.

I have told you of the front-page notoriety he acquired by his death—a notoriety about as welcome to us who loved him as would have been an attack of leprosy. One New York newspaper, in an editorial commenting on the story, said:

"And yet people speak contemptuously of 'dying like a dog!'"

I have told here perhaps three per cent of my fund of true dog stories; probably *less* than three per cent.

Have I bored you? I am afraid so. Have I made you understand and appreciate your own dog a little better? I wish I might dare to hope so.